en passant

"Freeze-frame pictures flicker past
the window of my carriage as it rattles on …"

en passant

A sideways look at life

Michael Polkinghorne

Matador
9 Priory Business Park,
Wistow Road, Kibworth Beauchamp,
Leicestershire. LE8 0RX
Tel: 0116 279 2299
Email: books@troubador.co.uk
Web: www.troubador.co.uk/matador
Twitter: @matadorbooks

ISBN 978 1788037 181

British Library Cataloguing in Publication Data.
A catalogue record for this book is available from the British Library.

Printed and bound in the UK by TJ International, Padstow, Cornwall
Typeset in 11pt Aldine401 BT by Troubador Publishing Ltd, Leicester, UK

Matador is an imprint of Troubador Publishing Ltd

MIX
Paper from
responsible sources
FSC® C013056

For Maura,
my soul mate who encouraged me to put pen to paper,
and in whose poetry I found great inspiration.

CONTENTS

My eleven years at school in Johannesburg on the same campus provided me with one of the two threads of stability in an early life of frequent and dramatic change often bordering on the chaotic. I lost my mother at age 13 and my father two years later. The other thread was the home provided by an aunt and uncle in my adolescent years. From them I was given a sense of family and, from my boarding school, one of order and discipline.

I progressed through school with reasonable, but unremarkable, success, perhaps best summed up by a not very academic classmate who once remarked to me, "You know, Polkers, I envy you because you are an all-round success". I did not take this as the compliment I am sure he intended, but rather as a comment on a lack of any particular excellence on my part.

Although I played all sports with enthusiasm I never made the first eleven or the first fifteen. And, whilst I trained hard in athletics, my legs were not quite as fast as some of the other boys so that, in the end, my only trophy in that field of endeavour was a small silver cup for winning the under ten egg-and-spoon race at my prep school.

It was obvious as I left school that I would not realise my boyhood dream of playing cricket for South Africa. So, in my first year at university, I took up rowing where, for a short while, I imagined I might finally achieve the sporting success that had previously eluded me.

I progressed quickly to the senior crews, won a trophy (another small silver cup) at a regatta on the Zambezi, and became vice (note 'vice') captain of the Natal University Rowing Club. While there I was chosen to compete in the Olympic Games trials, but a crew from another university, ironically the one where I had started rowing originally, won and went to Helsinki. Foiled again!

This much of my life story is reliable insofar as my memory is reliable. The autobiographical pieces in the first chapter of this book are less so, particularly those based on my earliest recollections.

Many of the other pieces, whilst masquerading as fiction, are drawn from real life experiences in some way. *The Tea Room* and *The Palm Court* almost certainly contain expressions of unfulfilled childhood desires for lascivious pastries. And, whilst only the pieces in the chapters entitled *Perhaps?* and *Brief Adventures* are probably wholly fictional, it is likely that even the latter contain elements of wish fulfilment.

Michael Polkinghorne - Tunbridge Wells 2016

I

Unreliable Recollections

I often wonder.

Despite being born a fourth generation South African I was always more interested in my English ancestry than my South African nationality. Even my father, who was educated at an English public school, cautioned me to remember who and what I was, but I am not sure that his advice made much difference.

On the other hand, it was perhaps because my paternal ancestry is Cornish, and having been brought up on the maxim that when a Cornishman looks across the Tamar he sees England rather than Devon, that even the 'English' part of me was ambiguous. However, that did not matter much because my Cornish ancestry gave me a sense of a blood line stretching far back into the mists of Celtic Britain and of my ancestors having been in Cornwall before the Normans, the Anglo-Saxons or the Romans – back in fact through Tristan and Iseult to the Phoenicians trading finewares for Cornish tin.

Against this timeline four generations of British blood mixing with British blood in South Africa seemed like a mere blip, or like a piece of elastic being stretched very briefly across the sea and then returning to its anchor point.

In fact this long view was so strong that when a friend, who was very interested in his genealogy, told me that he could trace his family line back to one of William the Conqueror's knights, I replied, "So you are not a real Englishman after all".

However, it was not just the history. There were the place names. When I first crossed the Tamar, by train with a young wife and an 18 months old son, it was like entering a foreign land with which I was already familiar. Names like, Trebetherick, Kinance, Trelights, Carn Kenidjack, Gwinear, St Enodoc and Polwheveral rang out like small pieces of perfectly crafted poetry.

Whilst I have done very little genealogical research myself, someone who has done so told me that a Polkinghorne first appears in written records in the early 13th century when one Robert de Polkinghorne petitioned Henry III for permission to use a coat of arms. Now that, I thought, showed great entrepreneurial spirit. A Cornish family of ironmasters (which is what 'Polkinghorne' means, I believe) would never have added the very French prefix 'de' to their Celtic name unless they hoped that, by 'Normanising' it, they would make themselves more acceptable in the eyes of a Norman-French king. And, it has to be said, even his first name, Robert, has a distinctly Norman-French, rather than Celtic, ring to it.

But the ruse seems to have worked because a coat of arms was granted.

Much more recently, however, in mid-Victorian times, James Polkinghorne kept the Red Lion pub in St Columb Major. Something of a dandy he is reputed to have strutted up and down the high street every day wearing a morning suit and top hat and swinging a silver-topped cane.

In addition to being a publican and showing off outside, James was a well known wrestler who, when he beat the Devonian champion in a controversial three round match, in which the Devonian used the fire-burned soles of his shoes to rip James's shins, he was declared the West of England champion. A bas-

4

relief plaque commemorating the event was subsequently set into an external wall of the pub where it sits to this day overlooking the street.

But I suspect he was probably a many times great uncle of sorts because, at much the same time my direct ancestor, John, a corn factor from Penzance, sailed to Natal there to receive an allocation of free farmland in exchange for a 10% tax on his earnings. He left with his son and newly acquired daughter-in-law, the daughter of a Devonian vicar.

Sadly, however, their lack of farming experience seems to have been a handicap because the venture failed and they went into horse trading instead. That didn't work either. So they went into politics – with considerable success. One of them became Natal's Minister of Finance while the other became President of the Natal Colony and received a major 'gong' from the Colonial Administration.

Then there is my voice. Many years ago a number of people told me that my voice was very similar to that of Alistair Cooke of 'Letter from America' fame. A touch of the Transatlantic, maybe, I thought, wondering how I had acquired it. But, as that great man passes from our memories, a new comparison has been found. Now, in more recent times, a few people have told me that I sound like Trevor McDonald. Now a little of the Caribbean maybe.

And so I continue to wonder who I think I am. Possibly Maura went some way towards answering the question with a pithy summing up. Maura was my second wife who I met when she was in the process of leaving the convent after more than twenty years as a nun. She was also very particular about observing social standards and was inclined to admonish me when she thought mine fell below an acceptable level. In the early days I replied that she needed to make some allowance for me since I was, after all, a boorish colonial.

Unfortunately that lighted-hearted response gave her a stick to beat me with on subsequent occasions. Depending on the level of my misdemeanour as she perceived it she would add other related adjectives to my original. So, in the worst case, I would be a boorish colonial South African Bushman. Had she added 'Cornish dreamer', her epithet might have come even closer to the mark.

Now, whilst I know of no evidence suggesting that we have any Bushman blood I have a certain regard for their society. Laurens van der Post, the great South African humanitarian, philosopher, and conservationist spent much time with the Bushmen in the Kalahari and knew many of them well. He reported an occasion when a long standing Bushman friend introduced him to his partner saying, "This is my utterly woman".

Maura loved that title, and her disapproval of any lapses in civility on my part could often be assuaged by my calling her my utterly woman. All the same I am not sure that that brings me any closer to answering my original question.

So who do I think I am? Maybe, after all, I am a boorish colonial South African Bushman with a soupçon of Cornish dreamer and some Transatlantic/Caribbean in my voice.

Maybe. But do you know what? I don't think it matters very much anyway.

"I am what I am, and that's what I am", said Popeye the sailor man.

THROUGH THE VEIL

There are disconnected image shards
that shimmer through the veil
when I was three or four;
a modest hillside house that's looking down
on Durban and the sea; a small back garden
with a Paw-Paw tree; a lusciousness of
big green leaves and humid humming summer;
my mother, small and neat, being carried
yelling round the garden by my uncle
while my father looks benignly on.
And Geraldine, my cousin, slightly older,
and more worldly, coaxing me indoors.
"I'll show you mine if you will show me yours".
I remember feeling unimpressed,
and fairly positive that I'd been done.

Then mornings in the baby class with nuns
at Maris Stella Convent; simple sums
and weaving coloured paper into mats.
And Mitchell's Park on weekday afternoons;
my nanny, black, rotund and patient as
a priest, would listen, still, as I instructed her
in meteorology, and told her how the wind
was made by God with windmills in the sky.

Sunday afternoons on Durban beach
with cousin Peter, digging in the sand
for pennies our conniving dads had hid
to keep us occupied so they could chat
or nap; then buying toffee with our finds
while our fathers buried further loot
for us to find again, and spend again;
and so extend their soporific afternoon.

The light that pulsed and flashed around my room
on clear-sky nights as lighthouse beams across
the harbour on the bluff rotated round
and found a curtain gap and flickered
on my bedroom walls.
On murky nights
the harbour fog-horn boomed across the bay
reverberating, muted in the mist;
its mournful moaning reassuring too
that all was well for me tucked up in bed.

At five I fell in love with Megan at
the kindergarten; slightly freckled, big
brown eyes and little dimples in her cheeks.
My father heard about her and suggested
that I add her to my bed-time prayers.
But love's sweet dream was ended when I tried
to save her from a bigger boy's embrace –
they sent me home with blood-nose in disgrace.

Nothing much was learned from Geraldine at four.
But, from Megan, as I closed the school-house door,
I learned that girls meant trouble
for a headstrong male.
But, after that, I went to all-boy schools
and adolescent hormones pushed the lesson
back behind the veil.

DEPARTURE

They say that very little memory survives from before one's fourth birthday so that, at four-and-a-half, the previous six months on my grandfather's farm would have represented most of my coherent life memories.

And, as a major part of my earliest period of organised experience, that vast area of hot, dry terrain in the Northern Cape, just to the north east of the Great Karoo, quite possibly also represented most of my world. That scorching sky, simultaneously blue and glinting gold, shrivelling the bush-land, against which the starkly silhouetted steel-framed windmill creaked disconsolately as it turned in the imperceptible breeze, struggling to draw from deep underground sufficient water for those who worked the farm.

Maybe it was these images, seemingly heightened as I wandered uncertainly around the familiar farm-yard searching for bearings for a life suddenly without fixity or meaning, that told me in some vague way that my imminent departure was also a kind of rite of passage; from this, my only world, to another which was to be my real world.

Standing awkwardly a little way off was Hans, the little African boy of about my own age and my constant companion throughout the past half-year. Alone and barefoot in shorts and singlet, and looking at the ground, his anxious hands twisted a soft sun-hat. Neither of us could bring ourselves to meet the other's gaze.

I tried the cart-shed where we had often played together, but the carefree laughter of two small boys climbing onto the large cart as it rocked on its squeaky springs was stifled in air already hot and pungent with the smell of horse-sweated leather, axle-grease and wood as the mid-morning sun irradiated the shade through the corrugated iron walls. As I turned I noticed Hans slipping away from outside the open doors of the shed.

But he was back again an hour later as we left in my grandfather's bronze Hudson Terraplane with its bulbous chrome headlights and wide running boards. He was standing near the big iron gates at the end of the dusty drive lined with eucalyptus trees in whose shade we had spent many summer hours. Our eyes met briefly, but our limp waves spoke only of a changing world. A new life was beginning; racial lines would be drawn.

Close to the Orange River we picked up the branch line between Douglas and Kimberley. There was no station, and the 'platform' comprised a strip of ground-level plank decking directly beside the tracks. Away to the west, shimmering in the late afternoon heat haze, I could see the Langeberg mountains which trapped the last of the moisture in the easterly air currents. On the other side was the semi-desert of the Great Karoo.

Separating out of the haze, and caught in the now low sun beyond the distant mountains, appeared a thin trail of smoke, followed by the lonely wail of a steam engine rolling across the reddening bushveld. A few minutes later the snorting brute clanked up beside us, hissing and rattling – gleaming in the sunset – its reason for stopping at this particular spot in the empty bushveld marked only by a few people on a small area of timber decking.

As my mother and I climbed some temporary staging into a coach, the sun was dipping behind a veil of steam on the other side of the train – curtain down on my life's first act.

HIGH POINTS, AND LOW

I grasp at memories, dissect, and then review.
The film-strips flicker, but they're not the ones!
Are moments of high happiness so few?

Okay; then stop the reels! There must be tons
of footage in my three score years and ten –
my cutting room of many moons and suns.

There was that near-orgasmic moment when
an early adolescent kiss cartwheeled
me crashing from a large oak tree. And then

there was that fifty on the cricket field.
I never made a ton, but halfway there
was good enough to have my team place sealed.

The time that followed moments of despair
when ten percent in arithmetic tests
had been my norm until the pea soup cleared,

and Mrs Tebbitt, beaming from her desk,
looked up and cheered, "Now, listen, class.
Who's got them right at last? You'll never guess!

"Old Polkers made it through the fog and passed!"

IN THE THICKET

It was just another bamboo thicket;
no more, maybe, than thirty feet by twelve,
between the boundary and the gravel path
that wandered through the garden to the church.

That's all it was, a clump of yellow staves;
unprepossessing, seeking no attention
from passers-by or garden volunteers;
rustling in the breeze, sorry for intruding.

But, out of sight, known only to himself,
a portal to alternate, secret, worlds.
In here, on castle battlements, he fought
to rescue maidens held by ogre kings,
or struggled on a dungeon rack in some
Teutonic fort to keep a password safe.
At Balaclava, sabre thrust aloft,
he charged ahead, and led the Light Brigade.
Falling on the gun-deck at Trafalgar,
he breathed his last with Hardy by his side
(though, even then, unsure about being kissed).
In wartime bombers, he was all the crew;
the pilot, gunners, and he aimed the bombs.
In Sherwood Forest by-ways, lay in wait
with Little-John – Will Scarlet with him too –
to rob the vile Sir Guy and feed a few
more Saxon serfs with rotten Norman gold.
As Blondel troubadour he rescued lion-
hearted Richard, restored him to the throne,
dislodged Prince John, and courted Marion
(forgetting they were nasty Normans too).

His thicket put him in the thick of it;
as buccaneer, with black eye-patch and cutlass
in his teeth, he scourged the Spanish Main;
a Cornish coastal wrecker, and a smuggler
dragging crates of contraband ashore,
then into hiding at Jamaica Inn.

And yet, somehow, his mother never knew;
just vague, and pleasantly surprised that, when
she called him for his meal, he came quite soon,
dishevelled, hungry, and always out of breath.

HALF TERM HARBOUR

"This rain's set in", remarked my mother
with the casual fey conviction
that comes when thinking doesn't intervene.
I often wondered how she "knew" these things;
but, ever since she forecast snow when
I knew she'd never seen it in her life,
I tended to respect her shaman musings.

The bamboo thicket in the churchyard
would normally have been my harbour.
In its labyrinth of passages
and shaded secret spaces that served as
gothic castles, galleons, and spaceships,
I performed heroic deeds and fought
with villains; rescued maidens in distress –
or found safe anchorage when seas were rough.

But all my fertile child's imagination
couldn't conjure up Saladin's tent
or Henry's canopy at Agincourt –
or anything to shield me from that rain.

So, for two long days, I sat beside
the leaded window watching silver
splashing from a pewter sky,
reading *Winnie the Pooh*, and *The House at
Pooh Corner*, and *William* – and wondered
how my mother knew about the rain.

TRAIN WHEELS AT NIGHT

Top bunk suspended and womb cocooned
in the rock-a-bye-baby creaking carriage
sliding dark through unrecorded space-time,
its heart-beat muffled over rattling joints,
platform lights from passing country stations
flitter bright through shaking wooden shutters,
the small boy dreams he's Drake at Plymouth Hoe.
Then, swaying in his hammock, partly waking,
his Mississippi steam-boat, hooter blowing,
steel wheeled carriage bumping, hisses to a halt.

Here electric power ends and steam begins;
men and torches on the platform urging haste
from those who tap the clinking wheels and shunt
the loco – couplings clanking down the train.
The steam-sighing silence in the frozen air,
before the zealous gasping pistons scream
and spin the wheels on icy midnight tracks,
then bite as coaches clatter; take the strain.
Outside the whistle's wailing in the dark;
within, the dreaming Drake is piped aboard.

DEFINING MOMENTS

The notion of 'defining moments' may be paradoxical. Aren't they more like *redefining* moments, because what we think of as 'defining moments' seem to modify, or release us from, previously held ideas of life or of ourselves? Surely our definition of anything must, by definition, depend on comparison with something else – something other.

In my case it seems to have been mainly girls. I had no sisters, few girl cousins, a mother who suffered a bit 'with her nerves' and, after kindergarten, I went to all-boys schools. So girls were strange and exotic creatures that I came across only rarely at birthday parties. I don't think I ever got the hang of them – not really – but I was always fascinated by their other-ness.

At kindergarten I got a crush on Megan. We were both five, and I received a bloody nose from a bigger boy when I tried to rescue her from his unwanted attentions. That taught me that the world is not as simple as it seems – especially when girls are involved.

Then, at about eleven, I kissed a girl in a tree – and the resulting shock caused me to fall out. That taught me about gravity – and the trouble that kissing can land you in.

By twelve I must have recovered sufficiently to try it again. The girl concerned acquiesced, but conditionally – on putting a toffee paper between our lips. It was OK, but not the stuff of falling out of trees – too much like wearing socks in the bath. I made a note to avoid toffee papers in the future. It was only in later years that I remembered that her father was a doctor and wondered if she might have misunderstood early advice on prophylactics.

At twelve I loved from afar, and in vain, the hazel-eyed girl in the Johannesburg Junior Orchestra. Not only was she older than I, but she was also the first violin sitting near the conductor, whereas I was a humble triangle player sitting at the back. She looked at me with cold disdain when the conductor scolded me for pinging my triangle at the wrong moment. That taught me about the power of status and that, if I had taken my piano lessons more seriously, and become a virtuoso, I might have been in with a chance.

THE PAINT BOX

That bitter-sweet feeling was there
when I pulled away the wrapping
and revealed the big, flat, shiny box –
when the conflict with wish fulfilment
was won by realism –

when I accepted that ten inches
by eight was too big to be true,
and that it was too thin
to be a proper paint box –

when I remembered that my friend
had one just like it,
a Joseph's box of sixty pallid colours;
thin little squares, dry and firm,
like pieces of delaminated liquorice allsorts
stuck side by side in six rows of ten
conceding at best reluctant globules
of pale liquid of uncertain colour
no matter how hard you scrubbed them –
and the box had a flimsy flat lid.

And when I wondered
if I should have been more specific.
But you can't really, can you?
You can't say the one I want
is about six inches by three
with no more than eight soft,
plump and vibrant colours in
little interchangeable ceramic pans,
and a lid that's moulded
into two or three bowls for mixing colour,
with a folding thumb ring underneath
so you can hold it like a palette.
You can't be that specific when you ask
for a paint box for Christmas.

BUNKING OUT

Gerry and I were finding that we needed some additional piquancy of risk each time we bunked out at night. To begin with, it had been enough to pad our beds with pillows and creep out to the cricket pavilion for a smoke – not a very exciting adventure although, if caught, both rule breakings would have meant expulsion.

But then there was the failure at Johannesburg Girls High where our plan had been to get into the school somehow, remove an item of underwear from a dormitory and hang it on the flag pole. However, the large brick fortress of a building protecting our sister school's boarders daunted us before we even made the attempt. So, rather lamely, we left our mark by overturning a few benches around the hockey field before walking glumly back to school.

We were clearly getting high on adrenaline–induced excitement, and were in need of a bigger "fix" each time. Neither of us cared much for smoking – our pavilion puffing was little more than low tar bravado. But, in spite of the Girls High fiasco, we had discovered that leaving the school campus altogether, and walking the well-lit streets of Johannesburg after midnight, added zest to the extra-mural experiences. And this probably lured us into ever more uncertain territory.

Going out in school blazers in the small hours was courting disaster, so the next project was better planned. By secreting sports jackets, leisure ties and soft felt hats in the cricket pavilion beforehand we would be able to change prior to sallying forth, this time to the cocktail bar of the Orange Grove Hotel. We even thought of disguising our ages, using a technique pioneered when, as under-fourteens, we had got in to see Jane Russell in the over-sixteen movie, The Outlaw, by smudging charcoal on our upper lips. Now, three years later, it was equally successful and enabled us to sit undisturbed for an hour or so sipping brandy and ginger.

However, it may well have been our experience on the way back that was to prove pivotal in bringing the adrenaline under control and an end to our escapades.

A wide tree-lined pedestrian way divided the large school campus, separating the school buildings and rugby fields on one side from the three boarder houses and cricket fields on the other. Our cocktail bar mission completed, we were sauntering back along this broad walk, when a figure appeared coming towards us. By the time proximity revealed it to be Mr Baraclough, the house-master of one of the other boarder houses, escape was no longer an option. By silent agreement we continued at our previous easy pace and, amazingly, passed the figure unchallenged.

Nor did we ever hear any more of the near-miss incident. But, after the fearful days that followed, we did ponder whether we owed our escape to the success of our disguises or to the possibility that the master himself did not wish it known that he had been abroad in the small hours.

GREEK TIME

Some years ago Frank Delaney, the well known Irish writer, was attending an international convention of journalists in Madrid, and was asked by a Spanish colleague if he knew the Irish word for 'mañana'. Delaney thought for a while before replying, "Do you know, I don't think we have a word that denotes that degree of urgency".

The Greek notion of time lies somewhere between the two, but with an angle of its own. The Greeks recognise the existence of punctuality, which they call "English Time", but accord it very little importance. A Greek friend once warned me never to use the term "noon" in Greece, citing the experience when a German failed to turn up for a noon meeting because the appointed time was insufficiently precise, and the Greek who, thinking it could mean any time between 11am and 2.00pm, arrived two hours late. It should be noted that he did not arrive one hour early!

I should have remembered all this when I arrived at Athens airport and made my way across the highway to the brand new railway station.

"May I have a ticket to Kiato, please?", I asked the lady at the ticket counter. Her face twisted into a mask of remorse in the way that only Greeks can manage.

"The train has just left", she said. "Since three minutes".

"Never mind", I said. "What time is the next train?"

"In one hour", she replied.

I looked at my watch. It was 3.00pm. So the last train must have left at 2.57, I thought, and the next one will be at 3.57. I paid for my ticket and walked over to the café on the other side of the large hexagonal concourse with its big glass lantern, and ordered a coffee and croissant.

At 3.50 I crossed the concourse and went down the escalator to the platforms. The electronic departure board over Track 4 announced the next three trains, the last of them being at 3.02. But none was to Kiato. With some concern I returned to the ticket office where I encounted a long queue of young Japanese back-packers whose English was more limited than the ticket counter lady's, so their negotiations took until well after 3.00pm. I had misssed the train, whatever time it was due to have left.

When I reached the counter the lady's expression turned to incomprehension.

"The sign on the platform said nothing about Kiato", I said.
"Because the train left at 3.45", she replied.
"When is the next one?"
"At 4.45. They leave every hour at that time".

There seemed to be nothing to be gained by pointing out that an hour from 2.57 is 3.57, not 3.45. It was an argument that would have little meaning for her and would provide no platform for a coherent discussion. I couldn't really blame the ticket counter lady. There would be more future in blaming myself for not remembering that Greek time and English time operate on different clocks.

THE FALL

*M*odern scholarship puts almost beyond doubt the probability that the story of Adam and Eve and The Fall had its roots in an earlier Sumerian tradition according to which the senior god Enki fashioned the first man from clay.

And the story of Adam's rib also seems to derive from Sumerian myth, that of Ninhursag and Enki. The goddess Ninhursag was angry with Enki for eating forbidden fruit in the Sumerian Paradise Garden of Edinu, and caused him to fall ill. Enki felt pain in his rib ("ti"), which in Sumerian means both "rib" and "life", and began to die. But Ninhursag relented, and created the goddess Nin-ti, a name which can be translated as both "Lady of Living" and "Lady of the Rib", to cure Enki. Because the pun of "life" with "rib" is present only in Sumerian, textual analysis places the Sumerian account as the more ancient.

In the Bible and the Qur'an we are taught that Adam (meaning, in Hebrew and Arabic respectively, "soil" or "man", and "living one") and Eve were the first man and woman created by God. The story has provided many of the most important symbols in Western culture including the Tree of Knowledge, the forbidden fruit and the serpent as Satan, and modern textual scholarship continues to analyse the story's many layers of meaning.

A further layer of interpretation might be added by my own experience of these matters; an experience that was almost Gnostic in the sense of it having provided direct knowledge, albeit more prosaic and less symbolic than the esoteric origins of the Bible story.

It was at a children's birthday party when I was about eleven years old and, most probably, we were playing hide and seek outside when I noticed a girl of about my own age in a tree. I had spotted her earlier, and something about her had given me a funny feeling inside. I am not sure if she was hiding in the tree, but I don't think it mattered. I just wanted to be there beside her.

It was not an exotic fruit tree – just a commonplace oak, and we were quite high up by the time I had settled on the branch beside her. But, once there, I was consumed by a desire to kiss her. I accomplished this feat without difficulty due largely to her willing, albeit passive, participation. In fact I can still remember the cool and quizzical, almost Mona Lisa, smile with which she surveyed me afterwards, as if she had just experienced something which, while being not unpleasant, was nevertheless of no great consequence.

But it was only a brief impression because, for my part, the effect was of an internal explosion of such severity that I lost whatever hold I had, and tumbled out of the tree, through the branches and onto the ground some way below.

I don't think I contemplated, as I lay there athwart a great serpentine root, investigating a painful rib, that I might have experienced the Fall from the Tree of Knowledge after an encounter with Eve. Nor, as I dragged myself up from the humus of man's creation and the thick layer of acorns, fruit of the tree, could I have realised that I had just received a foretaste of the knowledge which had been the downfall of Adam and Eve.

I just knew, and I remember this quite vividly, that the trauma of the fall, the bruised rib and the grazes, had all been well worth the experience.

*T*he Guard of Honour formed up along one long side of the large cloistered courtyard. At the centre, facing the scaled-down copy of Lutyens's Whitehall Cenotaph, stood the colour-ensign flanked by two colour-sergeants. Opposite, also facing the war memorial, and also occupying the full length of the courtyard, was a seated audience. On one short side a kilt-wearing pipe band was playing a lament.

At each corner of the wide shallow steps of the plinth around the Cenotaph stood a sentry with a shouldered rifle.

At a command at the end of the lament, the drum major turned smartly to face the war memorial and inverted his long silver-topped mace. At the same time, the colour-ensign dipped the flag; the sentries and the two colour-sergeants reversed arms – rifle muzzles resting on their left toe-caps – and bowed their heads. A lone figure stepped out of the shadows of the colonnade on the fourth side of the courtyard, raised a gleaming and betasselled bugle, and played the long haunting notes of 'The Last Post'.

As the melancholy strains, alternately languid and staccato, echoed and faded around the cloisters, and the bugler stepped back into the shadows, one of the colour-sergeants swallowed to relieve a lump in his throat.

On another command, rifles were shouldered, the band struck up the Regimental March of the Transvaal Scottish and, followed by the Guard of Honour, marched out through a wide arched opening into the large playing fields beyond for a ceremonial parade.

So, in 1950, ended the last Rememberance Day Parade in which I took part in my Johannesburg school's cadet corps.

Although the links with Britain were self-evident, for me this ritual was about more than that – it was about the Empire the symbols of which were everywhere around me during my schooldays.

My school had been founded in 1902 in a disused cigar factory immediately after the second Boer War in a frontier settlement that had not existed 16 years earlier and was, even then, not yet a town. Growing rapidly, Johannesburg College, as it had then become, moved, in 1911, to new purpose-built premises modelled on English public schools and, already with sufficient prestige to be granted Royal Permission, was renamed King Edward VII School following the king's death in the same year.

A few years later, the school's cadet corps became affiliated with a local regiment, the Transvaal Scottish, and its much prized colours were presented by the Prince of Wales.

Perhaps my feeling for the Empire was born of an understanding that, like South Africa and the colonies to the north of us, it happened largely outside Britain – in a sense where we were – and that it happened with drive, vigour and purpose. I was also very aware of how short our history was. My grandfather had fought in both Boer Wars, he had known Cecil Rhodes, who founded Rhodesia, and he had ridden with Jameson in his ill-fated 1895 Raid which had precipitated the second Boer War.

But it was also in my psyche that, as recently as 1886, on savannah land, originally roamed only by aboriginal hunter-gathering Bushmen, a township of gold prospectors' shacks had arisen which, in the space of twenty-five years, had evolved into a gold-mining proto-town containing a fine school in new buildings modelled on the best in the world.

And it was the 'Last Post' which, for me, was the thread that linked, and bound together, the territories coloured pink in my school atlas, and occupying almost a third of the earth's surface. I many times fancied I could hear the sinuously meloncholy sunset notes at military camps from Palestine to Mandalay, or at ceremonies in India, the Antipodes and Canada – places where, or from where, people of the Empire and Commonwealth had given their lives in a common cause.

Nobody could argue that the Empire was without blemish. It most certainly was not. But I nevertheless believe it represented qualities that were also Britain at its best – qualities that we seem to be ambivalent about nowadays, and appear to be willing to dilute or sacrifice in pursuit of some foggy politically-correct notion of multi-ethnicity or multi-culturalism. Perhaps we should instead simply try to ensure that those qualities become the undiluted glue of a homogeneous, unified and contented nation.

Last-Post-Script

In November 2014 the colour-sergeant, who relieved a lump in his throat in that 1950 parade, visited the Tower of London to see the art installation comprising 888,246 poppies representing all the Commonwealth armed services' lives lost in the First World War, and to pay his respects to them.

Remembering the threads that he had sensed bound the Empire of his youth he was struck by how many other threads there were in what he now saw as a complex fabric. Not least was the realisation that some of the poppies that filled the Tower moat represented old boys' from his school in Johannesburg and that more of them had been lost in the Second World War. And then there were the civilian lives around the world. The poppies in the moat seemed to be a metaphor for the blood of all those people.

There were thousands of people there that day, and it is estimated that a total of five million visited the Tower to see the poppies. Many would have been relatives or descendants of the war dead. He also lost an uncle in WW2. The blood of those who fell continues to flow.

Then he thought about the boys who took part in the Remembrance Day Parade in 1950, the years before that, and the years after that, right up to 2014. And it seemed like a time pod which is passed on year after year – repetition symbolising continuity.

"The Moving Finger writes and, having writ,
Moves on. Nor all thy Piety nor Wit
Shall lure it back to cancel half a Line
Nor all thy Tears wash out a Word of it."
(Rubaiyat of Omar Khayyam)

*I*t was probably while I was assembling the model plane that I realised it had not been a good idea. At first I took Mark's reluctance to having a petrol engined aeroplane for his birthday as being motivated by concern for the cost, completely ignoring the reality that a nine year old boy's only concern about cost might be that the gift was too cheap. No, I thought, as I slipped a wing into place, I don't think he actually wanted this plane at all.

I had noticed a shift in his position as we discussed the idea. He had seemed to move from reluctance to a kind of reserved approval which I had taken as a growing interest in the idea as the potential pleasure began to dawn on him. But there was never the outright enthusiasm there should have been.

Now, as he watched me connect the little engine to the propeller, I realised that he had been seduced by my own enthusiasm to a position of aquiescence, together, perhaps, with a reluctance to oppose his father directly on the sensitive matter of a birthday present. After all, it was only in fairly recent times that he had been consulted at all, and he may have felt uncertain about the rules in this unfamiliar territory. The implications of that thought bothered me more than the others. Had he felt that opposition might result in no present at all? Did he feel that he had been coerced? Had I in fact coerced him?

So, committed as I now was, I was determined to make the experience as pleasurable as possible and, if at all possible, to win him over. The assembly was completed during the morning, and the quick-drying paint hardened off during lunch. Then, with spirits raised by ice-cream and trifle, we all assembled on the back lawn, complete with our inquisitive cat, and I fired up the engine and launched the little aircraft.

The technique was to steer it away from the controller who, by keeping it flying against the tension of the control line, was also able to control its elevation and descent. All went well to begin with, and my heart rose with the plane as I caught a glimpse of the grin on Mark's face and the cat's head rotating as its big eyes followed in amazement the circular flight.

Was it because I took my eye off the plane that I lost control of its direction? Suddenly it was no longer flying away from me and, as the control line slackened, I was no longer able to affect its flight. With a kind of perverse will of its own, the machine flew into a steep climb until, running out of power, it flipped over and, looping into an even steeper dive, it crashed with laser directed accuracy into the cat, breaking its leg.

The howls of anguish and dismay, were exceeded by the shrieks of the cat as, bemused, terrified and disabled, it tried desperately to extricate itself from the scene of its trauma.

Not many people were speaking to me later that afternoon as they nursed the cat indoors, its leg in plaster, while I cleared the debris from the patio.

THE BONFIRE

*A*s the bonfire roared and crackled, the children jumped about squealing with excitement. When the flames reached the effigy of an unpopular politician, everyone cheered. And, as the effigy tumbled, my cue to start the fireworks display on the nearby scaffold framework, the crowd turned to watch the fizzing and shimmering introductory spectacle. They were not disappointed – not initially, anyway.

A stray spark from a taper lit the fuse of one of the fifty or more rockets arranged side by side on the twelve feet high platform and, before I could grab it and launch it properly, the hissing fuse had ignited its neighbour's fuse, and then the next, and so on.

In a flash, literally, the big rockets were bursting horizontally off the platform at three second intervals and streaking wildly across the field like night artillery illuminating the darkness beyond the bonfire where they exploded into brilliantly coloured sparkling light-showers. The crowd erupted into spontaneous rapturous applause believing this dramatic spectacle to be the first of many.

But, alas, they were deluded. That one accidental display had all but exhausted our stock of fireworks, and a thirty minute show had blazed out in barely three. As I tried to make something of a few desultory Roman candles and Catherine-wheels, a bemused crowd drifted away to the hotdogs and hamburgers near the smouldering bonfire.

*A*ll of us in the first year School of Architecture in a South African university struggled with our first design project – a kindergarten in a small country town. Not very complicated – a small hall, a small space for 'teachers', some equipment storage accommodation, and changing and toilet facilities.

But one of my fellow students rejected the intent of the project which was to see how best we could arrange a group of disparate 'boxes' so as to achieve a coherent and well functioning whole. Instead of rectangular boxes he saw these functions as being contained within curvilinear shapes. Needless to say he struggled to achieve any coherence in his 'solution'.

Whilst understanding the predicament he had created for himself, I felt that his attempt deserved some praise. But not so our studio tutor, an intelligent man with a PhD in Cape Dutch architecture.

It was only in my much more mature years that I began to wonder if his response was a symptom of a lack of emotional intelligence or of genuine understanding that the student was still too inexperienced to have it explained to him why non-rectangular shapes are difficult to manage in architecture. I am still uncertain.

Either way he turned from the display board on which the student's presentation had been pinned and, looking at him very sternly, he intoned in a thick Afrikaans accent with heavily rolled Rs,

"Boy, a rrright angle is called a rrright angle because everrry other angle is wrrrong!"

A major commission in Hong Kong required a substantial increase in my spending capacity to cover travel, hotels and consultants' fees in advance of any income I could expect from my client.

So I telephoned to make an appointment to see my bank manager. Except that he wasn't my bank manager. He was my 'relationship' manager who had telephoned me a few weeks earlier to introduce himself. The proper manager was apparently now looking after the accounts of the bigger businesses.

My relationship manager was obviously new to the job and enthusiastically offered to come round to my office to discuss my requirements. I declined his offer explaining that, since the bank would make a £200 charge for "discussing" my requirements, I was determined at the very least to get a cup of coffee in return from the exchange.

He turned out to be a young fresh-faced man in his middle twenties and, after flipping casually through my file, he announced cheerfully that there should be no difficulty depending on the level of uplift I required in my borrowing facility. The coffee was not particularly good and, being aware of the money the interview was costing, I was less cheerful.

Nevertheless I reminded him politely that my current overdraft facility was £15,000 but that, in view of the anticipated up-front expenditure the project would require, I would probably need to double that amount to £30,000. Once again he assured me there would be no problem – except for the interest rate.

He explained that I was currently on a preferential interest rate of 4% which, sadly, would have to be increased to 6% for any borrowing beyond £15,000.

"So", he began to explain with authority, "if you were to require the full £30,000 for a full year the interest will amount to …"

Here his authority failed him and, during the succeeding few seconds of silence I worked out that the interest over one year would amount to £30,000 x 5% (5% being the average of 4% and 6%).

"… £1,500?", I suggested completing his sentence for him.

He looked at me uncertainly for a moment then, excusing himself, he left the room. When he returned a few minutes later he placed a large calculator on his desk and, after clacking away for a while, he looked up at me and asked, "What did you say again?"

"£1,500", I replied.

"How did you do that?", he asked.

*D*espite being born into, and brought up in, a racially segregated country I don't think I was ever a racist in the sense of holding prejudiced views about races other than my own. It was more a question of accepting what was, for me, the status quo. I simply did not question the fact that I went to an all-white school, rode on all white buses or that white people sat on "Europeans (a euphemism for 'white') Only" park benches.

Later, in London, I remember wondering if I had perhaps been similar to a middle class boy in Victorian England in the way he might have accepted without question the "upstairs-downstairs" domestic arrangements in his comfortable Hampstead home.

Although the term "Apartheid" ('aparthood' in English, if there were such a word) had been coined in a speech by Jan Smuts in London in 1927, it was not in common use during my childhood and adolescent years at which time segregation was a strange kind of legally enforceable convention.

It was only in 1948, when Malan's right wing National Party won a general election and replaced Smuts' more liberal United Party that legislation was enacted and Apartheid became formally institutionalised. Sharpeville and the other violent events near Johannesburg did not occur until some years after I had left South Africa which may explain why my passive acceptance of the status quo continued into my early adult years. In fact I have very few recollections from that time which led me to any critical consideration of the subject at all.

One was the discovery that my clergyman father was welcoming Africans into his church at a time when this would have contravened the Apartheid legislation and when all the mainstream churches had fallen into line.

Another was when our liberal-minded Dutch (as opposed to Afrikaans) geography master asked the class an innocent sounding but, nevertheless, probing question; when considering the name of Paul Robeson, was our first thought of a great American bass singer or of a black man. The whole class admitted that a black man had been their first response. The implications of those answers came as a shock to me, particularly the realisation of the insidious way in which prejudices can hide in the recesses of the mind.

A third would have been funny had it not been for its dark undertones. During a purge on libraries and bookstores to remove books which were seen to condone or depict sexual contact across the racial divide it emerged that the investigators had been throwing out copies of "Black Beauty", the well known Victorian children's tale of a gentle horse.

Another was also almost funny, but this time tinged with irony. I must have been about ten when I was visiting a friend who lived in a much wealthier part of the suburb where I lived. At one point a black maid brought out a picnic for us and elegantly laid it out on a rug under a tree on the lawn. She herself sat a short distance away and, after a while, asked me where I lived. It was clear from my reply that she had identified not only that I lived in a much more modest part of the suburb, but also the house itself. "Oh", she replied in a voice laden with condescension, "Is that the house with only one servant?"

RELAXING

Sunday afternoon, midsummer, about twenty years ago. The Tunbridge Wells public refuse tip was even more primitive than it is today. Beyond the tipping wall lay three or four acres of stinking household refuse over which a couple of bulldozers ground their way grudgingly trying to spread the material evenly over the surface in preparation for landfill.

Present everywhere, hanging heavily in the hot sultry air, the stench seemed to throb like a slowly vibrating heat haze.

In the middle of this field of foetid decay one of the workers was taking his ease. Half reclining in a dislocated deck-chair, bare-chested and with a grubby baseball cap at a jaunty angle, he sat nonchalantly, one leg over the other, oblivious of the flies and the fiendish squawking of the circling rooks, reading a battered Sunday tabloid.

I wondered if, like the deck-chair, the paper was an old copy, rescued from the refuse, but decided that it mattered not. The content would have been much the same anyway, not unlike that of his surroundings and, in any event, the page three girl might, in his case at least, have been sufficient to anaesthetise him from their immediate effects.

*W*hen I was helping design the Chester Beatty Library Museum in Dublin I worked with Nabil, a Lebanese specialist in early mediaeval Islamic manuscripts of which the Library has many.

When Nabil moved from his university in Beirut to Manchester his new academic colleagues called him "Bill". He was a relaxed fellow and confessed to being quite happy with his new name as he was when he moved again to Trinity College, Dublin, where his colleagues changed his name once more, this time to Liam.

2

Perhaps?

THE BRIDGE

*H*ow can such subtle issues be defined, let alone decided? The pros and cons, too finely nuanced for critical examination, evaporate in the mind, disappear under inspection – wisps in the wind, like her breath on his cheek and the feather rolling lazily before him, rising and falling in the mist-drenched updraught pluming out of the gorge, turning this way and that, taunting his uncertainty, now catching the warm orange glow of the tree-filtered tropical sunset, now reflecting the dark churning cauldron in the chasm below.

And ahead, and in his head, the roar of the great falls thundering over the edge, smashing on ledges and bursting deep and dark into the seething maelstrom of indecision, where the waters writhe and fight for release and clear direction, and the trapped Fates boom and moan around the streaming crevices and jagged rock faces in the narrow twisted gorge.

Above the boiling tumult, the feather floats easily, twisting and teasing, drifting out of sight, reappearing, glowing with promise, dark with forboding.

The slender rope and bamboo bridge creaks and sways in the evening breeze, suspended uncertainly over the darkening gorge. For a time, the maelstrom mist obscures and softens all forms, and the feather is lost in a murky pall of billowing greys – trees loom briefly and sullenly on the banks and, between the shifting rockforms, lowering ominously at uncertain distances from him, familiar faces move, peering anguished out of the roaring tumult.

In the silver-sharpness and clarity of the full moon, the feather re-emerges, drifting in the opalescent lunar rainbow, glowing

in the long arcing wraith that streams from above the falls'
edge into the depths of the gorge. Drenched and weary, he
stares for a moment towards the side from which he entered
the flimsy bridge. Then, with a deep sigh, he turns, a lonely
figure, swaying in the moonlight above the pounding turmoil,
towards the opposite side. The feather, sinking now in the
cooling updraught, loops capriciously once or twice, glistening
brightly, and disappears.

THE DEVIL'S ADVOCATE
("Rules were made for the guidance of wise men, and the obedience of fools")

*D*ressed in a hooded sackcloth gown, she was led into a lofty space of ivory-coloured marble with gold inlays. In the centre, a softly-lit honey-coloured dome glowed ethereally over a circle of gold mosaic in a floor lit also by dappled sunlight filtered through arched openings to a gentle green landscape beyond.

Ahead of her, at an elevated white marble bench, beneath a gold silk canopy, sat a man wearing a white gown embroidered with gold designs. He was tall and dignified with flowing white hair, and steady blue eyes set in a finely chiselled face that was stern but not unkind. She guessed he was The Judge.

Near him, at a honey-coloured marble desk, sat a man in a pale blue gown whom she took to be the Clerk. He was short and portly, with a tonsured head, a round pink face and chubby hands. There were two other desks, similar to the Clerk's; one, empty, facing the bench and, the other, facing the Clerk, occupied by a man in a plain black gown. He was lean and of medium height, with a fox-like face, short grey hair, grey goatee beard and darting grey eyes. She had seen him before, and knew him as The Advocate.

The Judge motioned her to the empty desk facing him. Then he turned to the Clerk.

"Why are we hearing this appeal with this woman being represented by Lucifer's Advocate?"

"My Lord Gabriel, the Court of Ruling Angels found that she had broken the 10th Commandment, in that she had coveted her neighbour's wife. The Court was satisfied that she had been familiar with the Commandment, and dispatched her to another place."

"Yes, but then why is she up here again?"

"It seems, my Lord, that Lucifer's Court of Admission refused her entry at the Hadesian Gates."

"Oh! And why was that?" he asked the Advocate.

"They did not believe she had broken the 10th Commandment."

"Indeed! And the grounds for that belief?"

"Because she is a woman, my Lord, on the grounds that, since the Commandment was framed to protect married women from the attentions of other men, it cannot logically apply to a woman."

"Yes, I can see that we have the Devil's Advocate with us. Very well. Whilst that may be an argument of sorts, you should understand that, up here, we are considering a change of position on these matters. What was her sexual orientation?" he asked the Clerk.

"Heterosexual, my Lord."

"I see. In that case she was probably not guilty of coveting her neighbour's wife, so please remind me of the specific grounds on which our Court found her guilty."

"Specifically, my Lord, in that she had coveted her neighbour's wife's wardrobe."

"Ah! Then we have it," said the Judge. "The Commandment is explicit in forbidding the coveting of 'anything which is thy neighbour's.'"

"It is indeed, my Lord, but Lucifer's Court took the view that the wardrobe in question belonged not to her neighbour, but to her neighbour's wife, so that it is not therefore covered by the injunction."

"But is not her neighbour's wife also her neighbour?"

"Probably not within the meaning of the Commandment when framed, my Lord."

"Surely the Court of Ruling Angels did not send this woman down on the basis of this kind of labyrinthine argument?"

"No, my Lord. At the time, the case against her was supported by the fact that she had also coveted her neighbour himself. However, Lucifer's Court was dubious as to the extent to which the Commandment was intended to protect married men from the attentions of other women."

"But, if the coveting were reciprocal, then the man would be in breach of the Commandment, would he not?"

"Yes", replied the Advocate, "if the coveting were reciprocal, then it is possible that he would. But that would beg the question as to the extent to which the woman is guilty of the man's sin. Genesis 3:12 (Adam and Eve) is unclear on this point. But, further, since the woman is unmarried (and is therefore his neighbour, rather than his neighbour's wife) it becomes even more unclear as to whether he would have been in breach of the 10th Commandment wherein the injunction seems not to cover the coveting of one's neighbour as such. But, in any event, my Lord, the man is not here at this time."

"So, if she cannot go to Hell, are we obliged to keep her here?"

"Heaven knows, my Lord."

*T*he space is a soaring irregular volume – cavernous and somewhat domed, but neither cave nor cathedral – the height of a six-storey building, and over half the size of a football pitch at the base. Although the honey-gold walls are rugged, there is an order in their ruggedness. The surfaces comprise large sculpted rectangular sandstone panels of differing sizes, horizontally arranged, but asymmetrically facetted out from the background. In the low light the effect is of a golden glow, interspersed with dramatic shadows. And, in their architecture, there is a strange mixture of the primitive and the sophisticated – of the simple and the highly developed.

Balconies project from some of the facets, while stairs and escalators are suspended from others. And, between them in other places, narrow shafts of light slice through slit-like openings illuminating olive trees on ledges and slim cataract-like waterfalls.

At the top there is a larger opening where computer controlled reflectors monitor and deflect direct sunlight so as to maintain a low level of ambient light within. In so doing they create slowly changing patterns of reflected light on the ceiling which echo the changing moods of the sky outside.

A precisely controlled narrow beam of sunlight, discernible only in fine dust and smoke particles in the air, penetrates from top to bottom where it first illuminates a large piece of sculpture. The reflected light is then scattered by opaque white umbrellas so as to ensure that it is shed only on the cream marble at ground level. People are sitting at tables under the umbrellas. From here it appears that the darkened volume above is floating, hovering unsupported, over a vast concourse that disappears in all directions.

In the low light above, people can be seen moving up the stairs on one side, and down on the other. Some pause on balconies or on ledges, while others move in and out of openings between the facets. Images and text flicker on some wall panels, and on diaphanous screens floating in the huge open volume. Every half hour or so, the roof reflectors combine with mirrors and prisms to provide a dramatic light show of darting beams of pure white and rainbow colours.

From a platform suspended under the central roof opening, glass capsules convey visitors up and out onto shaded terraces over which a large asymmetrical glass tent protects the space below from the extremes of daytime heat. At night the tent can be opened to the purple-blue Athenian sky. Over refreshments on the terraces, visitors can view the ancient sites of Athens while being entertained by traditional Greek dancing or music.

This is an exhibition space, created for a wealthy Greek cultural foundation whose remit is to tell the story of Hellenic history and culture using the latest communications and design technology.

At floor level there is a small sunken amphitheatre for modest performances and teaching, and a lake into which, via a final waterfall, spills water from the cataracts above. A few trees grow around the rocky banks of the lake. The sound of moving water, the historic background to Hellenic culture, pervades the whole space, while periodic light shows are reminders of the brilliance of Greek sunlight, whose sharp shadows shaped their ancient architecture, sculpture and hard-edged logic.

And, although the space needs to be enclosed, the large sunlit floor area is a reminder of the open spaces, or agoras, in which Greeks have always spent their leisure time, while the scale of the volume is a metaphor for the scale of Hellenic culture and history. The hard shadows of the rugged walls hint at architecture, but they are also a reference to an archaeological excavation through which the visitor progresses vertically.

The visitor thus commences in the Pre-historic Period and moves upwards via stairs or escalators cut into, or suspended from, the "rock" faces through the Classical and Byzantine Periods, and Ottoman Rule, to the Modern State at the top. Each Period is characterised in a projecting balcony offering a different perspective on the subject matter in the main volume.

Suspended beyond the balconies are floating screens onto which short films and images can be projected and viewed from the balcony. Inwards, in exhibition spaces "cut" into the "rock" face, reproductions and models, together with audio-visual and virtual reality technology, offer the visitor further details and impressions of the particular Period.

Suspended for most of its height in the centre of the volume, a series of long vertical banners also act as screens for the projection of Hellenic images and impressions, from landscapes, through seascapes to people and history.

The downward journey is similar in design, but offers expositions on specific events, people and social history such as Alexander the Great, the Trojan Wars, Socrates, democracy, naval technology and domestic life under Ottoman Rule.

The exhibitions were intended to attract both Greek and international visitors and, in their initial stages, were seen by the Greek government as providing, with the Parthenon and the National Archaeological Museum, one of the three most important tourist attractions to coincide with the 2004 Athens Olympics.

Important design criteria included the avoidance of an over-simplified style reminiscent of Disney, or one that was too didactic. On the other hand the design acknowledged that material of this kind should be both intellectual and experiential. The space was thus conceived as a theatre of drama and experience in which ideas and information would be absorbed through as many senses as possible.

I was commissioned to develop the project from conception to completion, and I promised the client a result that would be world class, would become the benchmark for culture-based exhibitions in the 21st century, and the biggest attraction in Athens after the Acropolis. In fact, I made it a condition that I would do nothing less.

But, in the event, the client lacked either the courage or the vision, or both, and drew back from the scale of the concept outlined in the proposals. And so, one year into a five-year contract, I resigned.

And so, a big space remains in a small space in my head.

*H*e blinked in the low September morning sun as the commuter-packed subway station escalator brought him up to street level. Although not quite yet Fall, the air was cool enough to condense the vapour escaping from the Barclay Street drain covers into wisps of steam and disperse them into the light breeze that rattled a scattering of leaves along the sidewalk kerb.

Turning right onto Church Street he made his usual stop at Mario's delicatessen which, as always, smelled deliciously of coffee and freshly baked pastries. Mario was arranging blueberry muffins in a display cabinet behind the counter and greeted him without looking up.

"Hi Tony. Two bagels and coffee?"

"Thanks Mario" he replied, "but add some pastrami on rye."

"Sure! Hungry this morning?"

"No, the extra is for my lunch. Got a heavy day today."

He ate his breakfast at a window seat watching the office workers passing on the sidewalk outside and wondering if the old saying that you can never enter the same river twice also applied to a stream of people. He decided that it did. Then he thought of Rebecca and wondered if she reciprocated his feelings. He sighed a long sigh then got up to join the current on the sidewalk.

"Ciao", called Mario as Tony reached the door. He raised a hand absentmindedly in salute without turning. Different people, different stream he thought, as he stepped outside.

With no stops the express elevator reached the fifty-seventh floor in just over a minute. He blinked as he entered the landscaped open-plan office, half the size of a baseball pitch, and looked across at the long sun-bright wall of continuous glass stretching away on the far side with its panorama of New York City towards the East River from Brooklyn to Upper East Side.

But his mind was elsewhere and, having dropped his briefcase and lunch on his desk, he contrived a nonchalant stroll over to Rebecca's workstation.

"Hi Becky, you still okay for the ball game this evening?"

"You bet. I'm looking forward to it", she replied with a bright smile.

His heart missed a beat as he gazed at her, but she was looking intently at the window wall that had darkened slightly as if by a cloud passing across the sun. It was her hand grabbing his that broke his lovelorn reverie, and he turned to look in the same direction.

As if projected onto the ultra-wide screen of an oversized slow motion virtual reality cinema, the wings of the approaching four-engined jetliner stretched out of sight on either side towards the limits of the continuous glass wall. And, as the nose plunged into the building, he realised almost dispassionately that the flight deck would be entering two floors above.

But that was all he realised. The deafening explosion, the eardrum-splitting air pressure, the kerosene flames and the start of the progressive collapse of the structure all occurred in a zone of objective reality, beyond the reach of himself and Rebecca.

No one would have paid any attention to the palm trees rustling on the beach or the leaves scattering across the harbour road in the light on-shore breeze. And the smoke from the fish smokery always fluttered like that before curling back towards the town. Nor would they have noticed particularly the slight surface froth beyond the reef, or the thin line of mist hovering over the horizon far out to sea.

And, in the modest little weather station, slightly elevated above the town on the only knoll on the small island, the duty technicians were probably relaxing. This was not hurricane season, and the weather was clear, so there was no radio traffic through the flimsy antenna wobbling in the breeze above them. Even if they had scanned the horizon with binoculars, they would almost certainly have made no more of the mist than the fishermen preparing their boats in the harbour below. After all, low ocean mists are commonplace in this part of the Pacific. And, as for the froth, there was always some turbulence around those shallow reefs.

On the other hand, the fastidious mayor might have noticed the leaves gathering against a bend in the kerb where the harbour road turns seawards towards the ships' chandlers on the other side of the fish market, observing that the road had not been swept for a few days.

But that is speculation. We shall never know because, five hours later, no one on the island was alive.

They were much too far away to have heard the deep-throated groans and growls beneath the ocean bed ninety minutes earlier when one vast continental plate ground majestically under another in mid-Pacific, tilting as it did so. And they were too far away to have seen the resulting tower of water erupt from the surface to the height of a fifty-storey building. Nor could they have heard the deafening roar as the gigantic water column collapsed on itself sending a ten metre high wave racing across the ocean at a hundred miles an hour.

As the great wave entered the shelving shallows of the island, the energy dynamics changed. It slowed in pace as it scoured up the foreshore, simultaneously rearing up until a wall of sand-laden water thirty metres high lunged headlong across the beach and up the knoll.

———————

A few days later, an Australian Geological Survey vessel, investigating the aftermath of the tsunami, anchored offshore. Through his binoculars, the chief scientist examined what looked like a huge mole-hill in the sea. Nothing penetrated or disturbed the even contours of the mound of sand, silt and mud. But, refining the focus a little, he thought he could detect the thin mast of a radio antenna near the top. It was leaning to one side and appeared to be wobbling slightly in the breeze.

LEGAL OPINION

*T*he brass desk lamp with its green, glass-domed shade was the only light in the office. It suffused the Georgian walnut desk with a deep satin glow which also penetrated reluctantly into the recesses of the large room. A meeting table and chairs, and some low wooden cabinets further away against the walls, loomed ponderously uncertain, discernible only by the glinting highlights on their edges. Otherwise, their forms retreated into a background of mahogany wall-panelling whose only acknowledgement of the meagre illumination were the highlights on polished mouldings. In the far wall a large mahogany-panelled door in broad pedimented architraves glowered in the upward slanting shadows. A rich Oriental rug was just discernible on the dark polished floor boards.

At the tall windows behind the desk, blackout blinds concealed the splashes of orange and yellow flickering and writhing through the voluminous underbellies of the lowering clouds. But they could not exclude the crackle and crunch of the bombs bursting some way down river, or the distant bells of fire engines and ambulances.

Alone in the otherwise evacuated Whitehall building, his blanched face glowed like a death mask beside the shaded desk lamp. In front of him with its seal broken was the empty foolscap manila envelope recently delivered to him by messenger. It was marked, "OHMS. Office of the Secretary of State for Home Affairs".

But, holding his trance-like attention in the small pool of light were the contents – three sheets of paper. The first, stamped "Most Secret", was a summary of the trial and conviction for espionage of a twenty-one year old woman in the WRNS. The second was a plea for clemency by her mother, and the third, for his signature as Principal Legal Officer, a minute advising rejection. He turned back to the clemency plea. His spine chilled as he read again the name of the applicant and he slumped forward at his desk oscillating between disbelief and reverie in an anguish of torn allegiances.

The distant bombs and the crackle of anti-aircraft fire transported him back to a night in the spring of 1919 with Mary Buchanan, a young war widow, and the arts ball and fireworks display by the river in Putney – a belated celebration of the previous November's Allied victory. An evening of riotous revelry had preceded a night of passion in her flat nearby. Two young people, heady in the catharsis of peace and the abandon of new beginnings. But all was in flux then and, three weeks later, their brilliant starburst was a burnt-out acrid husk among the scattered ashes of their night of shimmering fireworks.

The desk lamp flickered as another bomb crunched, closer this time, somewhere near Waterloo Bridge. The windows rattled, and a trickle of ceiling dust sparkled as it drifted past the lamp. Startled, he focused again on the documents in front of him, hoping that the next bomb would be a direct hit.

Sighing heavily, his features sagging, he read the details for a third time. But there was no need. There was no mistake. The woman named in the Order was a Jeanette Buchanan, born 17th January 1920 in Putney, and the principal signatory to the clemency petition was Mary Buchanan, her mother, also of Putney.

Only when he heard the wail of the "All Clear" and noticed that the bombing had ceased and his mind began to clear did he lift his pen from its silver holder to sign the advice minute recommending refusal of the clemency plea. And only then, pen still in hand, did he raise his eyes above his illuminated desk and consider the ponderous shadows in the darkened room beyond.

———————————

Strangely, he was not altogether surprised by the sight of the figure sitting in the armchair near his desk, possibly because there was something about the man that reminded him of photographs of his grandfather. And there was something familiar too about the affected languid pose, one leg over the other, as if sitting for a painting. The chin rested easily against the curled fingers of one hand, the other draped nonchalantly over the arm of the chair.

He was wearing a bottle-green silk cravat below a winged collar, and his casually unbuttoned dove-grey frock-coat revealed an elegant gold watch-chain slung across his lavishly embroidered waistcoat. It was in the pose, identical to the painting hanging in the Council Chamber of the Bar Council that he recognised his grandfather, Sir Edward Marshall Hall, heroic Edwardian defence barrister, scourge of the Prosecution and famed for his incisive mind and courtroom histrionics.

The great man appeared to notice the recognition, and his expression changed from one of penetrating inquiry to sardonic amusement.

"So you have already reached your verdict?" he enquired with silky sarcasm.

"About my relationship to the condemned young woman?"

"What else? Is it not that which disquiets you so?"

"Is any other conclusion possible?"

Sir Edward raised a hand dismissively. "I see now why you withdrew from your short sojourn in chambers in order to make your career instead in the Civil Service in criminal and constitutional law. Here you are neither called upon to think on your feet, nor even, it seems, on your posterior. Of course there are other possible conclusions!"

"But the dates; the names!"

"Huh! Purely circumstantial!" The hand flicked sideways; a lace shirt cuff quivered. "Have you not perused the transcript of the woman's trial? As a matter of recent national security, I will wager that you will find it in your library next door. For Heaven's sake, man, read it!"

Obedient to the voice of authority that had cowed many juries and withered many a High Court judge who had sought to rebuke him for his courtroom showmanship, he retrieved the case of Rex versus Buchanan and returned to his desk. For a long while he worked expertly through the files until he reached the Defence, where a passage of questioning caught his eye:

"Are you Mrs Mary Buchanan, née Clark, mother of the accused?"

"Yes, sir, I am."

Née Clark! The young woman's mother's maiden name was Clark. But Mary's maiden name was Hamilton! The implications struck him like a bomb-burst and, looking up sharply, he met the steady gaze of Sir Edward, still holding the same pose, his mouth curled into a smile almost of derision.

"Well?"

"She must be a different Mary Hamilton. I remember Mary going to her late husband's brother's wedding in Putney soon after we met."

"And?"

"And, well, Mary is not exactly an uncommon name, is it? What if his bride's name was also Mary? Then Jeanette's mother is the other Mary Buchanan."

Relief surging through his wracked emotions, he rose and opened the blinds. The first rays of a summer dawn entered the room, its pink glow dissolving the sombre shadows. Near his desk, the empty leather armchair shone like a glass of Burgundy caught in candle-light.

*H*rodgar hovered in the shadow of the stone entrance to a barrow waiting for an opportunity. As the elaborate funeral rites nearby approached their climax and eyes were turned towards the pavilion containing the royal body, he slipped out into the bright moonlight. Using what cover he could find, he crossed the hundred yards or so towards the vast excavation and the reed caskets – each an overflowing cornucopia of precious jewellery, weapons and artefacts.

The great purple canopy suspended from a wooden frame over the excavation provided some shadow in the moonlight and, since all he wanted was a single piece of gold, he slithered the last short distance along the ground on his belly up to the graveside caskets. But, even in the shade of the canopy, the treasure glittered in the flickering light of the nearby braziers. And it was they that gave him away. As he grasped a broad gold shoulder clasp he heard a call of alarm.

He had anticipated this possibility but was sure he could outrun his pursuers and lose them in the fens he knew intimately. To begin with all went well, zigzagging through the moonlit reeded marshes towards a series of old wooden walkways spanning the broadest of the wetlands. He reached them ahead of his pursuers, but his luck ended there. A rotten platform collapsed and he fell through becoming trapped in the splintered boards and wooden framework. As he struggled a series of heavy blows to his head put an end to his life, and the gold shoulder clasp sank out of sight in the murky sludge.

Roger Marshall squinted across the Norfolk wheat field trying to relate the aerial photographs with what he could see before him. From the air he had seen some variations in colour and texture suggesting past surface changes, possibly the sites of ancient ditches and waterways. Although an Ordnance Survey map helped him track the line on the ground he saw nothing helpful until he reached a stile beside a fence in the far corner.

Here, untouched by ploughs, the earth was softer and darker and, when he knelt down to investigate, he noticed the familiar signs of ancient woodwork rotted into fibrous pulp which also appeared to continue on the other side of the fence. As he probed into the fibrous material his fingers touched a hard object. He withdrew it gently.

In amazement he recognised the elaborately decorated gold shoulder clasp as the twin of the one housed in the Norwich Archaeological Museum – part of the hoard from the late 6th century Anglo-Saxon royal boat burial site near Wroxham, and regarded as second only in importance to the finds at Sutton Hoo.

'This will do my doctoral dissertation no harm at all', he thought, as he climbed over the stile to investigate the other side.

But a rotten stile step broke and he fell backwards hitting his head heavily against a fence post ...

_____

... As he crept closer to the great ship lying majestically in the deep excavation, its gold decorated curved prow sparkling, the elaborate funeral rites were reaching a climax. The royal pavilion was opened, tall conical towers of timber around the excavation were lit and burning braziers were brought to the graveside.

Scores of women wearing long white gowns, bronze tiaras and masks appeared beside the excavation. Some sang a lament as they performed a slow swaying dance while others, whirling long flaming torches, wove in and out of the singers. Another group placed aromatic herbs and spices in the braziers.

Behind them in ceremonial regalia a troop of drummers beating slowly and rhythmically was drawn up beside the king's helmeted bodyguard ready to escort the royal body the short distance to the boat. Ahead of them stood the queen in a purple gown and wearing a gold tiara and stole.

As the smoke from the braziers and the powerful aromas mingled and swirled around the grave merging in turn with the dancing, drums and the rhythmic spinning of the flames, the midnight air seemed to erupt into a gyrating intoxication of singing lights.

… But why is he here, and why is he approaching the treasure in the graveside caskets just as the body of the king, borne on a ceremonial gold and silver battle shield, is being carried out of the pavilion by a dozen men clad in scarlet tunics and bronze helmets?

… And why is he running away and onto this moonlit walkway in the marshes?

… And what is he doing tangled up in this muddle of this woodwork?

… And why is his head hurting so badly …?

He moved slowly trying to extricate himself from beneath the broken framework of the stile. It was difficult because one hand was injured and the other was clutching the gold shoulder clasp.

*I*t started very softly, and very far away. Muffled grating moans mingled with deep sub-bass rumblings and growlings, rising and falling, then louder, booming and echoing as if in vast reverberating caverns far below the seemingly endless sun-rippled white icefield.

The four men stopped and looked at each other. Behind their face-obscuring ice-flecked beards and dark goggles, a mutual sharing of anxiety was palpable in their paused postures. The splitting of the Arctic icefield had never been considered a possibility, let alone mentioned in their briefing, but the sounds they were hearing seemed to signal the beginning of a major tectonic upheaval. There was no way of knowing exactly where the separation would occur.

Then, as the moaning turned to a grinding screech, their white landscape heaved and tilted by several degrees, and the low sun, which had been glowing like a huge orange balloon floating on a far distant flat horizon, disappeared behind a newly-formed jagged edge looming a thousand feet above them no more than two miles away.

They all lost their footings and fell as the fracturing icefield tilted, one of them letting go the tow-rope of his sled which slipped quickly backwards several yards into a shallow trough in the ice. As he picked his way gingerly down the newly formed slope to the sled, the icefield moved again, sloughing back slowly and pondorously with a long mournful sigh that seemed to him to express all the sadness of an ailing and weary world.

By the time he had grasped the tow-rope, and turned back towards his companions, his goggles were reflecting the orange glow rippling again across a level, silent icefield from a sun once more hanging peacefully over a distant horizon. Everything seemed normal once more, and the others began heading west.

He took a step forward to follow and, as the tow-rope tightened behind him, the landscape tilted again, more steeply than before, toppling him backwards onto his sled laden with part of the group's under-ice listening equipment. But, this time, the icefield remained at an angle, the sun once again hidden behind an even higher, orange-tipped, razor-edged horizon.

Now the problem was to drag his heavy sled up the slope to where his startled companions had stopped. It was not far, thirty paces at most. But it was steep, and he slipped and stumbled several times in the first few yards as he struggled upwards.

As he paused there, wondering what they would do in this new landscape, the sloping icefield convulsed and, with another rasping scream, broke its back along an uneven seam a dozen paces in front of him. Briefly he glimpsed his companions on the other side as they slid away behind the ridge where the two tilted portions of broken landscape met at opposing angles and rested on each other.

The world was changing. A few minutes earlier, this had seemed to be a vast and stable icefield. Now, he was alone on the slope of a broken ridge more than a thousand feet above a long-shadowed shattered icefield. His companions were somewhere on the other side of the ridge.

3

A Question of Time

"Good afternoon major. Sir Lionel is expecting you. He is over there in the Library with Miss Alice. Please go in."

The butler turned away towards the Dining Room leaving him on his own at the door. He paused for a moment and then reached for the brass door handle. It turned easily in his hand and had a comfortable and familiar feel; almost like a lever on a 12 pounder Howitzer.

"Hello?" he called softly, as the door opened.
"Come in, my boy. Alice fancied she had heard you arrive."

Through the part open door he could see Sir Lionel sitting opposite his daughter near a log fire in a broad open hearth. It was only a fleeting glimpse. Then the fire crackled.

With the crackle, the fire seemed to explode into a barrage of field artillery and, in the smoke of the blazing battlefield, he barely had time to fling himself aside to avoid a cavalry charge pounding past in a bloody tumult of sabres, lances and hooves into the rattle and roar of shell-fire flashing and bursting around him, before remounting his horse and charging, sabre aloft, into the Cossack cannons in a last attempt to silence the remorseless bombardment.

The orange flashes penetrating the acrid battery smoke ceased briefly as the Cossack positions broke. But there were others on either side and, as he wheeled to begin a second charge, a shell burst beside him. Man and horse hurtled together to the ground among the battle's carnage.

As the great beast sighed and slumped across him, he felt a dam burst and a deluge hurtle down a canyon, filling the gorge in an overwhelming onslaught. As the swirling cauldron boiled over the canyon's rim, flooding the surrounding plains, a melting Himalayan glacier shuddered and, bursting free of its scoured bed, thundered down the forested mountainside towards him in an avalanche of flailing ice shards and the splintered remains of great pines. A million escaping and agonised birds screeching in terror blackened the sky ...

Returning was excruciating – tossing and tumbling on a shingle beach in the sucking backwash of a tidal wave, clutching at debris to anchor his thoughts in the mad surge and hiss of incomprehensible impressions and after-images. As the roar of the receding surf subsided, and the debris clattered to a standstill, a white ball of sea-froth hovering in front of him slowly reduced and clarified to a white-knuckled fist clenching a brass door handle. Beyond, through a gap in the part-open door, he could see a log fire burning in a grate.

Somewhere in the distance a few words echoed.
  "Sir Lionel is expecting you. He is over there in the Library with Miss Alice. Please go in."

Clearer now, the brass door handle turned easily, comfortable in his hand.
  "Hello?" he called softly, as the door opened.
  "Come in, my boy. Alice fancied she had heard you arrive."

Through the part open door he could see Sir Lionel sitting opposite his daughter near a log fire in a broad open hearth. The fire crackled. He paused briefly, shivering, then entered the warm room, standing to attention and bowing his head slightly to each in turn.

Alice rose, and came over to him, taking his hand in hers.

"I have matters to attend to." She squeezed his hand gently and turned away.

Sir Lionel spoke first.

"Now then, my boy. Be seated, and let us to the purpose. Neither of us wishes to prolong the other's discomfort. You have asked to marry Alice. In that desire you have my blessing. But there is one condition, which is that you resign your commission in the Royal Dragoons and take a partnership in the family bank."

"But sir! That is impossible. My regiment leaves for the Crimea next week."

"I am sorry, but there will be no discussion. Without a private income you cannot afford to support her. So there is a simple choice. The Dragoons or my daughter."

He sank back into his chair as if under a great weight, looking towards the door through which his beloved Alice had recently left the room. He wondered briefly why he seemed to be fascinated by the brass handle and why it sent a chill down his spine.

Then he turned back to meet Sir Lionel's steady gaze, his mind oscillating between relief and anxiety.

"Very well, sir. I accept your terms."

DAYBREAK

There's a moment of no duration,
of neither one thing nor the other,
like the point of no tide at tide's turn,
or the moment of solstice when day is
at its longest – or shortest –
but only for a moment of no time,

when an arrow reaches its apogee
and hangs suspended and motionless –
for a moment of no time,
or when the sea temperature hangs in the balance
and a butterfly's wing can trigger
an El Niño or a hurricane – or not.

Or the moment when night's end
is balanced on a knife's edge –
neither night nor day – and silence falls
just before, if you are in Mandalay,
"the dawn comes up like thunder,
out of China 'crost' the Bay".

Daphne paused briefly in the passage outside the white panelled door and pondered the small rectangular silver tray she was holding. Checking the tray before entering had been part of her routine for several years but, for some reason, she had never before felt the need to contemplate it quite so earnestly.

On the tray, as always, was a finely crocheted doily, a cup of Assam tea and three Nice biscuits on a small plate. Although the inscriptions beneath were covered, she could visualise them precisely. In the centre of the tray was an oval cartouche with the monogrammed initials JPB, for Jolyon Peter Beaumont. Along the top were the words, "In Some Corner of a Foreign Field", and at the bottom, "Gallipoli, 25th August 1915". The tray had been a discreet gesture by Hermione twelve years earlier in memory of her son. But, sadly, life in the house had never been the same since.

Daphne listened for a moment noting that, although there would be activity in the kitchen two floors below, no sound penetrated up here. That's the way Hermione liked it. Somehow she still lived with the imagined clamour of battle on the beaches of the Dardanelles.

She turned and looked at the brass carriage clock on the small walnut and rosewood Sheraton table nearby. The hands were at two minutes past 8 o'clock. Knowing that Hermione also liked punctuality, Daphne wondered why she had not heard the clock chime.

Turning the brass door handle quietly she entered the darkened room. Hermione lay comfortably curled up in her wide canopied bed. The eiderdown was as smooth as it had been the previous evening. Daphne moved the water glass to one side and placed the tea and biscuits on the bedside table. Then she walked silently over to the window.

The heavy damask curtains rustled discreetly as she opened them just sufficiently to allow a narrow shaft of slanting sunlight into the room. She did not want to waken Hermione too suddenly. She paused there briefly gazing thoughtfully out of the tall Georgian window, first across the dew-sparkled lawns and then, past the copse beyond, to the village – its tile-hung and weather-boarded houses nestling in the crook of the curved high street shimmering in the moist air of the early autumn morning sunshine.

Her gaze returned to the window and, after pausing on the glistening filigree of dewdrops on a spider's web by the brick jamb just outside, it followed the dust motes circling slowly in the sunlight shaft down to the floor where a narrow strip of window seemed to be printed obliquely on the thick pile carpet – almost, she thought, like looking at an illuminated woven wall-hanging through an image of the window. She had not noticed before that the honey-coloured carpet contained a subtle pattern.

She turned and looked at the bed again. Hermione had not stirred. Strange, she thought. Normally the light from the window would have wakened her by now. She frowned and hesitated briefly. Then, deciding that she would look in again a little later, she turned and walked quietly out of the room.

LEAF FALL
A Meditation

How does it know when it's time to fall,
when, obedient to some cosmic mind,
it's time to break a season's bond,
to flutter russet-gold, to glide and twirl,
and float in Time
where past and present meet
and inter-leaf with future time
– for all is Time –
where leaves like this
have fallen, and will fall,
from trees like this,
and flutter down
to nourish earth for seasons hence
and seasons past
– for all is Time –
to nurture trees in other times
to rise and fall again in other times
where forests fell, will fall
in time?
And maybe,
once upon some other time,
I'll contemplate a floating leaf,
and wonder
how it knows it's time to fall.

TIME PIECE
(With apologies to Lewis Carroll)

"The time has come", the Clocksmith said,
"to talk of timely things;
of sundials, watches, water-clocks,
and whether time has wings;
if time can fly, stand still, be killed,
and if matter's made of strings.

"Now take the space-time paradox
of bodies moving fast;
if you overtake the speed of light,
you'll end up in the past!
Before the past there's only Now;
But how – and can Now last?

"If true that space and time are curved,
are they saucer-shapes or bowls?
And, is the universe a tube
of ten-dimensioned folds
with cosmic burrows plunging through –
those short-cuts called Worm Holes?

"Their kin, Black Holes, will swallow time
and space, and all they can;
they'll gulp in stars and galaxies
like spinning stardust-pans.
When space-time's gone, a speck is left –
and that's the next Big Bang!"

"This must be it," Megan decided as she looked across the expanse of horseshoe-shaped green and common enclosed by an extended crescent of Victorian houses. It seemed smaller now than it had when she was six; but she guessed that may be the result of 32 years in a sprawling Adelaide suburb. All the same, she remembered the way the green itself nestled like a half moon at the bottom of the arc, separated from the adjacent common by a footpath. And, down the nearside curving road, she noticed a small primary school on the edge of the common. That was new, she thought.

At the far side of the common Megan turned her car into the quiet Crescent, past the church and the pub, and parked beside the small parade of shops. The newsagents, where she had once bought sweets, had become a convenience store with a new façade. And the ironmongers next door was now a smart ceramics gallery. A dozen or so doors further on was the house where she had lived, but she decided to leave that for later.

She crossed the road to the footpath and, yes, there on her right was the cricket pavilion at one narrow end of the half-moon green, freshly painted for the new season. Near the footpath the groundsman was painting the boundary line of the cricket field with a trolley. He looked up and greeted her as she passed.

"G'day," she replied, "I hope it stays fine for you," and continued down the footpath towards the scout hut on the edge of the common. Then she pulled up short, startled. What scout hut? There was no scout hut! Only the primary school she had seen earlier.

She shivered, and looked across the sunny green for reassurance. There was the groundsman, a little further round the boundary but, on her left, the common felt cold and dark. Silly!, she told herself. It's only the shadows of the trees and, thrusting her hands into the pockets of her short Spring jacket, she carried on along the footpath.

As she passed the clearing in the common, loud mechanical vibrations and gratings, and the smell of hot grease, brought her up again, shaking and goose-pimpled. No way could that have been the lawnmower on the cricket field. She wanted to turn back, but felt compelled to continue towards ... she nearly said 'scout hut' again ... towards what?

But she couldn't bring herself to look into the common – not until the splintering roar of a great wood-fire, and acrid woodsmoke choking her lungs, jerked her head to the left – and she found herself staring at a split, but neatly trimmed, tree stump.

She was terrified now and turned towards the green again for security. The groundsman was on the far side. But at least he was there. At least that much was real. Or was it? Either way, she was beyond continuing, and sank limply onto a bench near the school.

———————————

Excited children's voices. Mid-morning break for the young ones at the primary school, and she hears them coming out onto the playground overlooking the common, laughing and calling to each other. She is elated by their exuberance, and drawn into their excitement and delight as they run and skip between the fairground attractions, climbing on and off the big whirring carousel with its bucking horses, or telling each other about the helter-skelter and the chairoplanes.

She and Janet are running with their candyfloss past the spark-flying, clanking and bumping dodgem cars to get on the big wheel, when she feels the first drops of rain. She looks up, and sees heavy storm clouds darkening the early evening sky. The coloured fairground lights seem brighter, and the tinny organ music more strident.

Lightning flickers between the clouds, and a sudden roaring bolt of brilliance flings her to the ground – and the lights go out. Nearby, the big oak blazes wildly and burns to the ground in seconds in a shroud of crackling smoke; and the rain pours down in torrents. In a tumult of thunder and screaming children, she runs for safety.

"The scout hut; the scout hut!" she calls to Janet, but Janet has fled the scene, so she runs alone and climbs the few wooden steps to the door of the raised scout hut. It's open! As she stumbles headlong into the hut, another flash mangles one of the metal supporting posts, and half the structure collapses. For a split second, as she shouts for help, she sees roof beams falling …

———————————

"Megan! are you alright? Are you alright, Megan?" Urgent voices are calling in the darkness. She is surrounded by debris. She tries to answer, but her head is swimming.

"Madam! are you alright? Are you alright, Madam?" The darkness clears, and she opens her eyes. The groundsman is leaning over her anxiously. She smiles weakly.

"Yes, I'm alright now, thank you. The sun is shining on the common."

He looks at her oddly. "Are you sure you're alright, Madam?"

HARRY

She flopped onto the settee and burped. Then she hiccoughed and giggled. It had been quite a party. "From foster-child to chambers," one of her colleagues had said during his toast to her.

She had enjoyed that. It was both accurate and succinct; its brevity spoke to her rapid progress, and she liked the alliteration. Certainly she had done well. From being fostered before she was four, she had arrived in her twenty-seventh year as a criminal law barrister in chambers in Lincoln's Inn, with a brief as junior counsel in a case at the Old Bailey. She giggled again, and hiccoughed.

Through hazy eyes she noticed the red light flashing on the answerphone out in the hall, but decided to check her messages when her head was clearer.

Her grandfather clock – a much loved oddity in the contemporary "corporate" style furnishings of her Russell Square flat – chimed the half hour. She turned her head and the hands on the mottled sepia face told her it was two-thirty. 'Past my bed-time' she thought, getting up unsteadily. But, instead, she went over to her cocktail cabinet and poured herself a large Cointreau on ice.

On the way back she paused and steadied herself beside the clock she had had for as long as she could remember. She stroked it lovingly wondering how she could repair the scratch below the face. It was the only link with her misty past and, without the family she yearned for, it was all she had with which to share the joy of this moment; this new beginning in her life.

But what was her past? Before the age of four, memory is soft and lacks the fixative of understanding. All she could ever see were back-lit stage figures moving behind gauze in shifting spotlights: noise, anger, fear; and a small figure – always that small figure. Then her kindly foster parents, the Thompsons, her teddy bear and her huge clock. She stroked it again. 'How did I come by you, and how did I manage to hang onto you?' The slow ticking, loud in the near 3am silence, spoke only of the twenty-three years they had been together – but not when they had met, or what had happened before. As always the story ran from the half light into the shadows – and her eyes glistened.

With the help of an armchair she moved back to the settee and slumped into the soft matt black leather, spilling some of her Cointreau. "Bugger!" she muttered as she placed the glass clumsily on the table beside her. "I apologise, m'Lud. I withdraw that last remark to the witness." She giggled, lay back and closed her eyes …

————————

She jumped, startled, when the telephone rang. She seemed to be on the stage again with the strange figures moving about her. But where was the small one? Her head was light, yet her uncoordinated hand was leaden as it fumbled awkwardly for the phone. She lifted it, waiting silent, her heartbeat and the clock's ticking merging and booming in her ears.

"Hello?" It was a man's voice. "Hello? Harriet?"
"Yeees," she answered tentatively. "Who's speaking?"
"Hello siss!"
"Who is this?"
"It's your brother, Harry. Your twin brother."

She gasped and slammed down the handset. As the silence crowded in, and the slow relentless ticking of the clock swelled and roared inside her, the figures stopped moving and stared at her inquisitively.

The phone rang again. She started, but left it. Some way off she could hear the same male voice on the answering machine.

"Harriet, it's me Harry. I'm sorry if I frightened you. It's very late and I guess they didn't tell you about your twin brother when we were separated. How can I convince you that it's me and that I've been searching for you? Do you still have the grandfather clock with the scratch under the face? I did that with a toy gun. Remember? Please call me back. My number is 020 99247 6753."

———————————

There were the figures again, moving in the changing light behind the gauze – and the small one. She tried to get a better look but he disappeared behind one of the others. The slow regular beat of the ticking focused her mind, and she looked at the clock again. It was three forty-eight, and she was cold. Beside her on the table was the barely touched glass of Cointreau. The ice had melted.

Out in the hall the red light on the answerphone was still flashing. She walked over hesitantly and, after a nervous pause, pressed the playback button.

"You have one new message," announced the formal recorded voice. "Message received yesterday at 7.18pm". A second later she heard Mrs Thompson's familiar voice.

"Hello, dear. This is Celia. Just ringing to congratulate you on the new job and hoping you have a lovely celebration party tonight. I've probably missed you, but we can catch up when you have a moment. Goodbye dear."

A click, and the recorded voice spoke again,

"End of messages. You have no more messages."

*A*big orange sun smouldered above the sea's horizon, and the huddle of harbour buildings shone like jostled ingots as we crossed Fore Street to the Golden Lion. We had little more in our minds than a pint of St Austell bitter before some mussels in white wine and seafood chowder. It was busy inside but, with our glasses in our hands, we found a table away from the bar in a corner illuminated by a sunset shaft glinting through a harbour-facing window. The man already sitting there was about my age and height, but leaner and more suntanned. In what I recognised as a South African accent he invited us to join him.

"Thanks", I said, raising my glass. "This is my son, Guy. Are you staying here long?"

"No. Just a couple of days. A short holiday in these parts exploring my ancestry."

"Here in Port Isaac?"

"No, I'm heading off to St Columb Major tomorrow, and then on to Penzance."

"Interesting. My son and I have ancestral connections in those places as well. And after that?"

"Depends what I find. But probably back home to Cape Town."

"Ah, yes, Cape Town. A beautiful city!"

"It is indeed. And a great place to work. I had an architectural practice there before I retired."

"Oh, you're an architect? What kind of work were you doing?"

"Museums mainly. One of my last projects was helping to convert Robben Island into a heritage centre."

"That's a coincidence. Or is it synchronicity?"

"How do you mean?"

"Well, I had an architectural practice in Kent for many years, specialising in museum design around the world. I tried to get into the Robben Island project myself, but couldn't persuade Winnie Mandela that I was indispensable. Did you train in Cape Town?"

"No, I was at the University of Natal in Durban."

"Now, there's another coincidence. I did part of my training there. We seem to be of similar ages, so we must have overlapped. You're kind of familiar, but I can't say I remember you."

"Well, I was there alright. In fact I met my future wife there. We were fellow students."

"I wonder if I knew her?"

"I doubt it. Elizabeth Turner. A local girl."

"I don't believe this."

"Why?"

"You don't mean demure Elizabeth who went to the Maris Stella Convent in Durban?"

"Yes. In fact we got together on a rebound after I was jilted by a girl from the Transvaal."

"This girl from the Transvaal; she wasn't by any chance a ballet dancer by the name of Shenagh was she?"

"Might have been." He stood up and paused, thinking. "Yes, I remember. I'm sure she was. But, hey, will you excuse me for a moment, while I find the gents? Must be the beer."

I watched him go over to the bar where he was motioned to a door on the far side. Guy looked at me quizzically.

"What was that all about?"

"I wish I knew. I'm trying to get my head round it myself. Elizabeth and I were an item for a time after your mother, then a ballet dancer from the Transvaal, dumped me, a poor student, in favour of a young chemistry graduate with a good job in a pharmaceutical company."

"That's too much altogether!"

"Yes, it is. It's exactly what I was thinking."

"So, what happened then?"

"Well, some months later, the girl from the Transvaal thought better of her choice, and contacted me and, after a period of correspondence and re-evaluation, we resuscitated the relationship. So in the end Elizabeth Turner became the jilted victim."

"And after that?"

"Well, I had previously decided to finish my training in London, and that seemed to be a good moment to make the change. But, instead of me going on my own, we decided to get married and go to England together. As you know, we never went back, and the girl from the Transvaal later became your mother."

Guy looked at his watch, and then anxiously towards the doors on the far side of the bar.

"I wish your chum would hurry up. I really need to know how he fits into all of this."

"Believe me, so do I. But let's give him the space of one more pint. I'll get three more shall I?"

The last rays of the sunset flickering uncertainly off the harbour into our corner vanished as we drained our glasses. We stood up, looked at each other in silence and then moved towards the dining room next door. The third pint was untouched on the table.

4

Philosophical Musings

PEACE PIECE

Meditating on Peace –
Better than "researching" because
peace is a definition-defying illusion,
like "happiness" –
a mirage – the accidental by-product
of other aspirations and endeavours
which vaporises under scrutiny
or when pursued for its own ends.

Better than "researching",
which implies a hard-edged objective reality
"out there",
Peace requires ruminating, musing or meditating
on what is
"in here".

What is the quality of Peace which priests
invoke to be "with us",
and, regarding which, we reciprocate?
That which Muslims call upon
their Prophet, and even abbreviate
after his name?
Or that which is preserved by
a "peace-keeping FORCE"?

And what is its gender?
Why, I wondered, do ships,
traditionally female,
become "Men of War" when they fight?
Are they fighting to protect something feminine?
Or is that an old-fashioned sexist view?

But I decided that Peace was
of the feminine principle –
not exclusively female,
but of the principle
in which balanced men have a minority share.

Jung would have been a good source –
Better than Freud on the female principle.
But, instead, I turned to that place
of unstructured international musings,
the Internet.

Options led to more options,
and one stray click of the mouse
(or was it a Freudian click?)
brought "SEX" in big bold letters onto my screen
(Freud had arrived ahead of Jung)
just as Maura walked into the study.
"So that's what you do when you're alone in here",
she said matter-of-factly and,
having retrieved what she wanted from her desk,
she withdrew without further comment,
as if the incident had passed entirely from her mind.

Now, this was a kind of Peace I thought –
but definitely feminine –
and of the inscrutable variety.
But the Peace of Tantalus.
The fruit-laden branch above,
and the pool of water below;
both forever out of reach.
Do I attempt to explain how "sex"
came to be on my computer monitor –
and betray some kind of subterranean

guilty conscience –
or remain silent and leave lingering doubts?

But this is the very stuff of Peace.
Tension and uncertainty.
The over-taut wire between opposing forces –
transient and fragile.
What other kind of Peace can there be
in a Cosmos predicated on restless change
and violence?
We are the stuff of that stuff.
Best keep our heads below the parapet
And stay stumm –
Or look for it within.

FREEDOM?

Incarceration's over, so he signs
the forms that say he's free to leave
these walls; to step outside and walk new paths –
or tread the well-worn tracks with no reprieve.

He packs the remnants of his past – his life's
extent – in one old case; then snaps the catch
and takes the cash to tide him for a week
or so, as sullen men release the latch.

No good-bye greetings, fond farewells or smiles
to light the grey outside; no friend in tears
to whisk him off to some warm hearth and give
him back a little of his long lost years.

No, just the mist – and somewhere past the gates,
a limousine with darkened windows waits.

POST WAR

Empty
Battlefield mud
Cold moon on aftermath
Glistening firmament will renew
In time.

SILENCE
A Meditation

In the foothills of the French Alps,
between the Drôme valley and Grenoble,
ancient hamlets grew
out of the sandstone hilltops –
reflecting the massive fortress outcrops
on the higher mountains further east.

Here there is silence; a living silence,
an ancient peace we carry in our hearts
which, in places like this,
we find we have not lost.

The people in the hamlet live this peace;
courteous and quietly self-possessed
as we walk through their narrow street
of honey-sandstone houses
topped with Roman tiles of cream and ochre
smudged with rose
that melts seamlessly
into the hillside path beyond,
with its wall of natural sandstone,
weathered, split and fissured;
and, to the west,
the wide sweep of the Drôme valley below.

Here is the great silence,
where you can hear your heart beat above the sighing
of the mountain's breath among the grasses
and the distant goat bell;
where the great eagle

soars in the air currents
watching for the smallest movement on the hillside,
and where the Drôme, a trickle now in late summer,
flashes gold between the rocks
as the sun dips flaming behind a distant ridge.

RYE HARBOUR REFLECTIONS

When feet fall soft on inland dykes,
and sea-less sea-beds either side
– grass-gold, seamless, sky-to-sky –
whisper sad
with nearby shingle-sighing surf
of bygone days and future times,
of flooding seas, receding tide;

when, thought suspended,
sunset silent in the hide,
mind stilled in quiet contemplation
– glinting lake-edge ripples burning,
calling birds to roosts returning,
sweeping flight-paths curl and glide –
then… all are in Creation's Tide.

5

Diverse Verse

THE CORNER CAFÉ

I noticed her behind me as I queued
for coffee and a croissant. We hadn't
seen each other for a while, and I paid
for both our coffees at the counter.
At a table she passed some change to me.
"There's twenty pence too much here,
and I haven't any change", I said.
"Let it be in payment for your company",
"But I normally charge much more than that!"
"I don't think we should go there", she replied.

YOU GOTTA KNOW THE RULES

The M&S dinner for two was £10.
So I chose a main, a side and dessert –
to do me for two meals, I thought.
"That will be £11.78",
said the checkout lady.
"But I chose a meal for two for £10!"
"I think it's the cheese", she said.
"It doesn't count as dessert".
"But look, it says it here; 'dessert',
from the cabinet marked 'desserts'".
She stared at it helplessly,
then called her boss.
He said it was because I had no wine.
"You need to choose a bottle of wine
from the cabinet over there".
"So…, if I add a £6 bottle of wine
to the charge of £11.78,
it will reduce to £10?" "Yes", he said.
And, lo, so it was.
All but 5p extra for the plastic bag.
A good result, I thought.

THE SCALLYWAG CAFÉ

I ducked into the Scallywag Café
to dodge the rain.
New to me – on the other side
of town from my normal haunts.

Eccentric and eclectic
with no two table sets the same.
Double-fronted, big bow windows
looking out across the Common
and onto London Road.
Two earnest couples deep in laptops
and, reclining in a big armchair,
a youngish lady with a magazine.

I spurned a curved piano stool
beside a large clay pot with bright glass top
and chose instead the flimsy lightweight chair
belonging to a wrought-iron bistro set.

Soon after that, the armchair lady left
and smiled engagingly at me.
I wondered if she knew my rearmost
belt loop was caught up in a wrought iron curl
of my chair back right behind me.

I had to wait for the manager
to bring my cappuccino and unhook me.
"It's either that or I take my trousers off",
I said.
He chuckled. "I like that.
'Come into the Scallywag and get hooked'.
I think I'll put that on my website".
The rain had stopped by the time I left,
trousers intact.

WINTER SUNRISE IN KENT

Moisture and silence
hang heavy;
earth and sky without form,
palely luminous,
vapid in the void.

Equally equivocal, a bird tests its voice.

Swimming tones of grey;
No sun, no colour in this dawn;
only a slow lightening of its leaden-ness
– and an answering bird –
hint at its irresolute approach.

"ROUND MIDNIGHT"

Footfalls echo stillborn on the sidewalk flags
in winding-sheets of mist around my feet
and short-lived smears on glistening slabs beneath
a streetlamp's yellow fuzz-ball looming low
in moisture-laden midnight freezing air
that steams the breath and dulls the feral din
of cats who screech and brawl in upturned bins
and crates behind the closing burger bar.

The shopfront shutter clanks, and latticed light
marks out a court for pavement hopscotch spurned
by sullen, lounging beer-can-sucking youths
who turn away and slouch around the back
and fall among the bins and hissing cats
with loud guffaws. A first floor window light
appears, glows frosty half across the road,
my footfalls stillborn on the glistening flags.

GIRL IN A CHEMISE
(Reflections on the painting by Pablo Picasso)

She looks away, aloof, no mind to speak;
her features fine, some brittle beauty's there;
a lifeless arm hangs limp and incomplete;
her passive frame's inert and doesn't care
about the pale chemise that clings to her,
one breast revealed, the other not at all;
in light that's cold and gives her no allure,
she stands before a chilly blue-green wall.

Belle dame sans merci and devoid of fire,
Picasso was tormented in his trial
to find some spark of life for his desire,
your ambiguity to reconcile;
and so, in desperation, painted thee
sans breast, sans arm, sans sexuality.

THE BOW OARSMAN

Three backs ahead
of him glide back
towards the rear
(the slender stern)
on sliding seats –

he's close behind
the back in front
and slides in time
light hands on oar
with arms outstretched
he's forward reaching
taut legs folding
knees to shoulders
tiger coiling
brute strength pausing –

eight hands rising
four blades dipping –

the water's caught
and limbs explode
projecting hips
towards the bow –
the water's torn
the boat's propelled,

oarsmen leaning
horizontal –
a nano's rest

then dropping hands
flick clear the blades
with diamonds flashing
from the edges,
churning whirlpools
rushing rearward,
sharp prow rattling
over ripples,
seat slides whirring
under oarsmen –

as backs in front
glide back again.

CROSSING THE ALLENBY BRIDGE
(From Jordan into Israel)

Iron bolted girders span the Jordan,
iron gripped in history's repetition,
suspended in the currents of oppression,
sullenly buttressing east and West Bank;
a connection opposing connection.

Near this place marched the Medes and the Persians;
Roman Legions dismembered Judaea.
But lo! Now are the Israelites Romans;
now is Judaea divided by iron
and divided is Abraham's seed.

DEPARTURE OF THE NIGHT TRAIN

Last slamming doors as late arrivals board.
A whistle wails above the engine's hiss;
its echoes, mingling with escaping steam,
go whispering among the great steel vaults
suffused in grimy years and evening dusk
as slipping wheels catch hold and start to drive,
clanking couplings stretch and take the strain
and well-oiled pistons sigh their slow good-byes.

Silent film-strip lighted windows moving;
Freeze-frame pictures gliding, inching past me,
final waves and hankies on the far side.
A large man wrestles luggage in the lobby,
stows it on a bag-rack in the carriage,
flops into a seat beside a beauty
who shrinks away behind her Country Life.

A steward lays the table in the Pullman;
fresh white linen over polished walnut;
Counsel reads his brief, a scotch beside him;
who's the woman in the boa? Can't be
Lady Packham, can it? No it isn't.
Those two brats are fighting in the passage;
One gets smacked and throws a tantrum
knocking whisky over Counsel's trousers –
the smell won't help his case in court tomorrow;
squire looks up, annoyed, and blows cigar smoke;
soppy courting couple notice nothing.

Windows flicker; images are fleeting.
One car down they've started on their starters;

there's a party drinking bubbly while the
steward serves the vicar – sparkling water's
safer as he polishes his sermon.

Far ahead the locomotive whistles
as a blur of lights is disappearing round the bend;
smoke and steam still gusting round the platform;
in the darkness buzzing tracks fall silent.

THE TEA ROOM

Fine-boned, precise and prim Miss Havelock,
pedantic even, like her fragile Spode
that tinkles at eleven and again
at four, is mincing through the tables
as she takes the orders of the ladies
whose company she longs to share, but can't –
her very shop, at once their meeting point
and firm transparent screen, keeps "trade" apart.

"Darjeeling, Mrs Prendergast, or would
you like Assam today?" she fawns. "I'll be
with you in just a sec., Miss Jones". Behind
her pastries glitter in the cabinet
on long-stemmed silver salvers, oozing cream
and fruit and chocolate sauce, and drooled upon
by two small boys in prep school blazers, caps
and mangled ties being straightened by their aunts.

Her cut-glass smile glints disapproval of
the crumbs she flicks from linen freshly ironed
brightens just a little as the door bell
tinkles its hello to Lady Lyon.

"HAPPY BIRTHDAY DEAR AGNES"

Late afternoon, late misty autumn's gloom;
a few reluctant shop lights, glowing wraiths
above their soft-edged alter-egos
phosphorescent in the moistened pavement bricks.

The teashop's closed, and so, at half-past-four,
the weekend high street's cemetery quiet;
no resting place or fare for weary
travellers passing by this way;
no tea and scones.

Quite far behind, an urgent figure flits
from side to side, from shop to shop; now lost,
now reappears; it hastens back and forth
but gaining ground until it draws abreast,
an agitated teenage girl, who asks
if we can play the piano down the road!

Surprised at first, then Maura answers, "Yes,
a bit, but somewhat out of touch". "That's great",
says she. "It's only for a party in
the hall. My Gran is ninety, and the aunt
who should have come to help us sing the toast
has not turned up." The guests were in a state
with glasses poised in silence waiting for
the music; so if we could help them wish
her Happy Birthday, they'd be very much
obliged. "OK", says Maura and we turn
and trundle down the hill.

Bright parish hall's
alive, festooned, beribboned and ballooned;
wide-eyed anticipation; tables laid
with party fare. Guests "Whoop!" when we arrive
and rush the pianist to the stage, and fill
her glass. A moment's pause, she tests the keys,
begins to play, to lead them all to wish
the birthday girl good health. They sit me at
a table, give me tea and cakes; my plate
is full. Across the room I see her right
hand tinkling out the melody, her left
hand swings aloft to give the beat, and holds
a sloshing champagne flute to add her cheers.

THE FRAUDULENT ARACHNID

Since Arachne, as a weaver,
presumed to challenge great Athena,
and was turned into a spider
for her hubris and her lie,
the fraudulent arachnid
has spun webs of superstition
trapping humans as securely
as she ever caught a fly.

Running t'wards you portents trouble
but, on clothes or on your body,
she means luck or even money –
plus, tomorrow brings a letter.
If you spy her in the evening
climbing up her silken ladder,
or while spinning in a doorway,
your good fortune's even better.

Me? I think it's all baloney;
I don't throw salt across my shoulder;
as for walking under ladders,
there's no other could be bolder.
But the stone at Blarney Castle,
I believe in on my life;
it's not eloquence I'm seeking,
I'm just frightened of my wife!

THE MEETING

I must have missed her in the crowd
that poured in from the Customs Hall.
But she saw me, and went to call
an air hostess to check me out
 – was I who she thought I was? –
I said I was, and had ID;
so the lady left the girl with me;
my niece of fifteen from Natal.

I smiled hello, and kissed her cheek.
But was my hug too much? I know
we'd barely met but, even so,
she was my god-child, wasn't she?
Then, why so like a limp rag doll?
Was it flight fatigue? Timidity?

I wondered if I should have known.
Perhaps my gesture'd been too quick.
But, hey!
Without a girl-child of my own,
I couldn't know what makes them tick.
I smiled again. "Are you okay?
Alright then, lass, I'll take you home".

MOSQUITO PATROL

The jump beside me woke me with a fright
and, in waking, knew I'd heard a slap.
"Did it get you?" The voice put on a light.
"No", I croaked in simulated sleep.

But she was out of bed and on patrol.
"Where's the damn mosquito thing?" I heard.
I knew she meant the swat, but said no word.
Then, finding it, she said, "It's on the stool!"

"They're smart, those little devils, hiding there.
He was there when I went out, but now he's gone.
I'll bet he's there behind your bed". She scraped
the swat behind my head. "He's gone again!"

In time she gave it up, returned to bed
and pulled protecting sheets above her head.
Too hot for sheets for me; I'll take the bites.
Much rather that than have a sleepless night!

THE FOUNDRY IS SILENT

The foundry is silent;
skeletal remains
beside its slag-heap burial mound;
blast-furnace surrendered to the dark.

The crucible is cold;
only dust trickles, occasionally,
bat brushed from gantries,
moonbeam caught.

ANGER

    Anger came
in chariots from Hell
with screaming wheels,
flashing harness,
teeth-bared bits
and staring eyes;
with frothing horses
pounding blind
on burning hooves
on blood-soaked ground –
    and went again.

    Anger came
in slender, pointed icicles,
glinting frozen,
shiny-sharp –
    and stayed awhile.

NORTH CORNWALL

Wood-smoke ripping out of cottage chimneys
swirling into streaming roof-top clouds;
sheep – disgruntled, veiled in slanting rain,
contemptuous backsides to the wind –
graze by stunted hedgerows scoured leafless
and bowed obedient to Atlantic gales.

Below the craggy rain-soaked cliff path
waves exploding onto harbour walls
fling stinging foam on salted roof slates –
a rock-fall village in mute resistance
by the quarry face, wrinkled and scarred,
hissing and spitting its defiance at rain
retreating in sheets across the platt –
to writhing waves that spume the street.

RAIN

"Mean rain", Maura called it. Driven
ramrod horizontal underneath umbrellas,
penetrating fine stuff, in your face,
saturating on a windy evening.

Different from the drizzle on the motor
showroom forecourt – gleaming runnels coalesce,
swelling bright on shiny well-waxed bonnets,
then wobble loose like quicksilver, trickling
carefree, gliding into other globules,
skating skittish off the slippy surface,

or raindrops rustling through a Patmos palm
and dripping brightly on a summer square;
in pools of liquid sunlight café awnings
shimmer in the breeze that clears the sky.

MY GLASS OF WATER

This liquor, distilled, recycled and brewed
ten billion times from primordial ooze;
matured in the wood within rain forest trees,
rinsed in the rivers and soaked in the seas.

Aerated in rapids and great waterfalls;
breathed out as vapour to rain-bearing clouds;
fomented in flood-plains, in wetlands and swamps,
stirred by tornados, tsunamis and floods.

Rested for aeons in vast polar caps,
in slow creeping glaciers and icebergs afloat;
filtered through layers of sandstone and granite,
and stored in cool aquifers deep underground.

Clear, without character, body or nose;
urbane, unpretentious, but vintage mature,
this stuff of the comets, right here bottle-fresh,
winks at me coyly through fine crystal glass.

CAUGHT!

There's a tugging on my Waitrose wire
basket, and I turn to find an anxious-
looking lady slightly stooping, shuffling
strangely crab-wise right behind.
I wonder what she's up to, then I see
her jacket button's caught inside
my basket's wire mesh. "Oh dear", I say, while
pausing briefly for a cheeky line like,
"Do you really think you should be hanging
onto me in public quite like this?"
But the line eludes me so, deciding
safety is the better part of clever,
I release her gently with apologies,
and carry on towards the meat and fish.

HIS VOICE

She looks up, quick eyes darting wide, alert.
She hears him somewhere near the hall, and gasps.
But why's his voice so hard – so coarse and flat?
Not at all like him to speak to her like that.

Through kettle steam she sighs relief and smiles.
Of course it wasn't him; how could it be?
He's in Munich at the moment, isn't he?
Then, once again, that harsh demanding rasp.
A knock? Of course! The postman's at the door.
"Just one Recorded. Sign and print here please."

She takes the crisp white business envelope;
a logo in the corner and a name
in copperplate. Below in smaller script,
"Divorce Solicitors" is all she sees.

HOW DARK WAS THAT NIGHT?
"The Universe was forged out of darkness"
(Professor Jim Al-Khalili)

How black was the black in the moment
before the Big Bang,
when, dark in the dark black yard of a void –
no more than a point frozen in zero time –
where a moment was forever
and forever, a moment,
and black holes, dark matter, curved space and light
 – and multi-layered universes –
were just thought-forms in a pregnant point
of everything and nothing?

How dark was it then;
how black was the black
in that night-moment of frozen time –
before the Big Bang?

DEAD LETTER BAG

Sidling sly along the Hyde Park bench
towards the woman at the end –
his thin thighs tight together,
prim beneath his case –
while looking forward, blank,
as if the park were empty space,
apparently not noticing
they're touching shank to shank.

His fingers, neat, unlock the case,
withdraw a sandwich box,
and then an envelope – slipped quick
between their touching thighs –
while nibbling with distaste
his low-fat cottage cheese on rye,
still staring stolidly across the lake
with vacant eyes.

She shows no sign of contact –
not even mild surprise –
intent instead on press reviews
of films by Eisenstein.
But her surreptitious fingers
slither down between their thighs
then slide the envelope into her bag
beneath her copy of 'The Times';
then rising, pausing,
finger squeezing deep inside,
she leaves without a glance
at crimson ooze upon his chest,
loose jaw or staring eyes.

THE PLOUGHMAN'S LUNCH
(A Cultural Exchange)

"This relish is delicious, by the way,"
smiled the Stateside lady as she tried
her unfamiliar ploughman's in the pub.
"What's it called again? Brownstone, did you say?"

"Branston," I explained, and spelt the name for her.
"Could I get a jar of it in Harrods?"
"A bit too modest for their shelves, I'd say".
"Gee, you mean that Harrods is too fancy?"

She lost her smile, or was it a reproach?
So I bought a jar of Branston Pickle
at a grocer's after lunch,
and gave it to her as we joined our coach.

"Gee, thanks a bunch; please let me pay."
"My pleasure, ma'am; adds relish to our day".

THE CONTEMPLATOR

The classical statue nestles
by a bush in the park in St Germain.
Male, naked, larger than life,
half reclining, eyes cast down.

"Do you think he's contemplating
the origins of the Universe?"
I ask
"It looks to me as if he's
contemplating his penis",
she replies.
"Is there any difference?"
I ask.

CORNWALL REVISITED
November 2012

Now the TV crews have left the set
and headed home,
Port Isaac's pretty much the same.
The Golden Lion still serves the local fish
and crab and Doombar beer they brew
along the coast nearby.
The wet fish market by the harbour smells
the way it always did,
but slightly gentrified these days.
Now they'll cook your lobster while you wait
– a posher kind of chippy for the swells.
The cafés, galleries and shops
that tumble jumbled down the hill
have gone upscale a touch
but, otherwise,
Doc Martin hasn't changed Port Isaac much.

Polzeath is still a family strand,
but also now a surfer's dream
with surf-gear shops,
and surfing lesson kiosks on the sand.
One wonders all the same
if family fun's been lost at sea.
The new folk there don't fool about
play games, or laugh with glee –
they're far too earnest
in their pewter wetsuits as they stride
across the beach towards the breakers
clasping shiny surfboards to their sides.

The Padstow waves
some say that Rick Stein made
seem no more than beneficial ripples now.
The lanes and harbour-front
have had their facelifts
but haven't lost their charm somehow.
All the same some smarter harbour cafés
are serving cappuccino frappés.

The ferry from Bodinnick sails
the ancient course across to Fowey,
on the sailboat bobbing estuary,
rising closely clustered from the quay.
More upmarket now than I recalled,
its A-List visitors seem prone to leave
a record of their visits on the wall
as in the harbour bistro where
a menu hanging in the toilet's
signed effusively by Tony Blair.

OUR BARBER'S SHOP
(Reflections while waiting to be served)

We have a 'proper' barber's in our town;
old-fashioned spiral pole and all that stuff.
But there's just one thing – it's "manned" by ladies
who insist they're 'barbers', not hairdressers.
They'll cut anything, including ear-hole hair,
and give a foaming cut-throat razor shave
with steaming face towels from the microwave.
Then, while you're lying helpless in the chair,
they'll slap your razor-burnt and moisture-
softened cheeks with stinging spirit after-shave –
and relish it as well, as I can see from here.
Not my scene! That stuff rings no bells for me.
I mean, to pay a girl to slap your cheeks?
With cream? No chance!
You sure?
Hang on for a mo' – let's see.

BESIDE THE TRACKS

Freeze-frame pictures flicker by the window
as my carriage rattles past and on
through Mitcham, Morden, Merton;
with those small back gardens
coming right up to the fencing just below
the fern-filled wooded railway bank;
their postage stamps with franking
that for Freud reveal the minds behind the blinds
and curtains, lace or Roman; where
pedantic little Versailles gardens gleam
with light as fountains blur with cabbages
next door and potting sheds, a patio
with flower beds, exquisite little lawns
and stripy awnings, castellated small
extensions, haciendas with pretensions,
and a big Kew Gardens greenhouse share the
margin with abandoned bikes, old iron
beds, discarded prams and broken toilet pans
dumped casually on Southern Railway land.

THE COAL FACE

Here it is. This is it. The pit stops here.
This is all there is. No room for spin
between pick point and the wall of craggy jet.
No time for rebranding when the going's
getting tough, And, as you raise your pick,
there's no way that you can say, "we need to
leverage resources here, and then touch base
off line". Or, when you hear that tell-tale groan
and creak above your head, you can't just say,
"we need to push the envelope out on
this to mitigate the impact challenge".
And, when pit props are assembled to support
the fractured ceiling, you really can't just say,
"let's get the hampster back on the wheel".

MAURA

"She's a gift from God",
said my friend when he met her first.
Yes, she was in the convent
twenty years and more.
We all knew that. But he'd seen Beyond.
I was not surprised –
only that he'd seen so soon.
But then, why should he not?
Her blemishes were few –
transparent spirit almost.
And he had seen right through –
as through a glass clearly –
and then Beyond.
But now God has called her back.
So she was only a loan after all.
But we had her for a time.
And that was a gift!

I THOUGHT I SAW HER

I thought I saw her yesterday
standing at a bus stop
as I drove through Langton Green;
same build, same height, same hair;
same white blouse and turquoise
floral skirt she used to wear.
But it wasn't her of course.
It was someone different,
someone not as pretty, standing there.

IN MEMORIAM
(On Maura's birthday)

She hated winter with a vengeance.
Not because she disliked cold,
although that was a part of it.
Maura was an earth-child with an almost
pagan view, I often thought.
So, to her, the winter was a kind of death.
After all, it was in winter, she would say,
she'd "laid out" nuns who'd passed away.
" I mourn the sun's retreating in my
being's core", she wrote; but of summer:
"The bird within me soars to freedom
in the sky".
A poignant irony, then, that the dates
of her beginning and her end
should be a bare three dozen days apart –
and span the winter solstice.
On earth she may not easily
have gone along with:
"In my End is my Beginning".
But I believe that, in some summer place,
the bird within her soars in freedom
in the sky.

6

Africa

AFRICAN DAWN

Long before pale-peach blushed coy behind
the eastern hills; while stars still glistened bright
in violet velvet above the wraith
of moonlit mist across the water-hole,
stark white, glowing; and a haze of pewter
nestled in the coarse savannah grass –
the smell of arid earth, the aloe tang
and eucalyptus in the air, commingled
with the cloying scent of sweet marula
trees and kudu dung around the water-hole,
foretold another scorcher in the veld.

Then, slowly, as the sky began to fade
from violet into purple and stars dimmed
imperceptible above the western ridge
to sounds of waking kudu in the bush,
a dawn breeze rustled through acacia trees,
a fine brush-painted thin pink line lit tops
of eastern hills then streaked along horizon's
width, and coral flowed across the land.

In seconds, so it seemed, the great plain glowed;
a softly billowed rose angora shawl
was lightly draped across the water-hole
while, westwards in a sky turned mauve from
royal blue above the ridge, a few weak stars
still shone, but pale and wan.

But only then, when flaring disc was part
above the hills with orange chasing gold
across the veld, and silhouetting gnarled
the bare thorn trees, and glinting water-hole
became a ruffled rippling crucible,
and silence hung –

did the kudu move out timidly alert
with flicking ears towards the water's edge,
their brown striped markings ruddy in the dawn,
their shadows stretching past the hoof-trod pools,
sparkling on the muddy margin, towards
the dawn-pink spoonbills wading farther on.

KULULU THE HARE

(A personal creation based on the exploits of the African folk tale character known also as "The Little Wise One" because of his cunning exploits)

Part 1

How Kululu was trapped by Impanga

*K*ululu sat drowsily between two warm stones not far from the river bank. He had just eaten well, and he licked his lips, still enjoying his dessert of mealie meal and the memory of its acquisition. He chuckled with delight as his soporific eyes closed lazily in the midday heat, a light breeze ruffling his grey fur which almost camouflaged him against the stones.

He could still see Mrs Abafazi chasing him madly out of her yard after he had stolen her mealie meal, and he chuckled again at the thought of how he had manoeuvred her into letting him get to it. After feasting in her cabbage patch, he had moved as close as he could to where she was grinding corn on a large flat stone outside her hut and then, deliberately loudly, he had tackled yet another cabbage.

Alerted, Mrs Abafazi had flown into a rage and rushed into her cabbage patch, flinging stones and pans as she went. While she was doing so, Kululu had circled her hut and helped himself to the mealie meal, simmering like porridge in a large black pot over a fire. He had known that later it would be mixed with lumps of meat to make putu for the evening meal, but he wanted to get to it while it was still vegetarian. His appetite was already satisfied, and his delight complete, when she had turned from the cabbages to find him half inside the pot. With no missiles to hand, the large woman could only shout and scream while Kululu had ambled nonchalantly away into the long grass, and the river beyond. Once there he had chosen a stretch well downstream from where the women of the village washed their clothes on the riverside stones.

Dozing now, Kululu was slow to react to the sound of rustling grass nearby. Nevertheless, he was alert enough to remain quite still and survey his surroundings through half opened eyes. And, yes, to one side, not far away, he spied Impanga the fox, partially hidden in the long grass, his eyes glowing yellow with anticipation and amusement in the African sun as he watched his meal taking a siesta.

But he enjoyed his anticipation a moment too long, giving Kululu time to compare his distance from Impanga with his distance from the stones in the river. As Impanga's eyes focussed for the attack, Kululu bounded from one boulder to another until he was sitting out in the middle. Even though the rainy season had not yet come, and the river was still low, he knew that Impanga would not risk the water. So, with the fox now at the bank, they eyed each other in mutual disdain, both knowing that Kululu was trapped while Impanga remained.

His eyes glinting again in anticipation, Impanga settled down near the water to wait. Kululu did the same on his rock. He yawned widely. "Have a good rest, Impanga", he called. This time he could allow himself to sleep properly, for he knew that his night vision was much better than Impanga's.

Part 2

How Kululu escaped from Impanga

Darkness was falling on the sluggish dry-season river and the pools, shining like crucibles of molten copper trickled disconsolately from one to the next, darkened to glinting anthracite as the big African sun slipped below the horizon behind the eucalyptus trees.

Sundown comes quickly in this region and, quite soon, as long shadows from the wooded bush beyond the tall grass fringe crept across the bank where Impanga the fox was lying, a light evening breeze drifted across the river carrying with it the smell of wood smoke and the sound of nearby villagers preparing their evening meal.

On his warm boulder in the middle of the river Kululu's whiskers twitched as his sensitive nostrils picked up the smells from the village. They told him that for the time being the villagers would be occupied with their meal leaving their vegetable patch unattended.

Impanga also remained at his post near the water's edge, strategically positioned close to the rocks which he knew Kululu would have to cross to get back to the bank.

But Kululu was aware that his long wait was nearly over and that with the darkness would come his chance of escape. He opened an eye and peered into the darkening bush where, as he expected, he could see a small group of impala waiting nervously to move down to the river. Impanga worried them, but having decided the fox was an unlikely predator, they ventured out of the bush and made their way timidly, ears flicking, towards the well trampled muddy water's edge.

And he had also been keeping an eye on a partially submerged rock in the shallows not far from where Impanga was lying, now wide awake, and watching as a young impala, spotting a larger pool nearby, wandered in that direction.

As he watched the rock lashed out of the water and huge crocodile jaws seized the slender neck dragging the buck writhing and thrashing into the water. Kululu's nonchalant gaze shifted to Impanga who was standing stiff legged quivering in terror before his survival instincts carried him yelping into the bush.

Kululu's whiskers twitched again as he rose casually and made his way across the boulders to the bank, where he turned and sauntered downstream towards the nearby village. It was quite dark now, and the people were gathering around a large black pot set over an open fire. So he knew they would not be watching their cabbage patch.

SECURITY IN GOLD

Lioness lazy; dappled gold
glowing warm in Kenyan sun;
killer teeth not bared, but hold
a smile; her cub at play
is bested by his brother – only fun,
but runs to mother; "am I OK?"
Lethargic cuff, a sideways glance,
sees no hurt and yawns;
"no problem son".
Eyes glow golden –
Breeze-blown whiskers dance.

THE RELIEF

(A personal recreation of a tale overheard from my grandfather who fought in the Boer War – a 'vlei', pronounced 'flay', is a small shallow seasonal lake in the South African bush)

O nly when the great glowing disc of the sun, vast compared with its size at midday, spread orange from end to end of the wide horizon, as it dipped into the low distant hills, soaking the great plains of the veld in gold, and making gnarled silhouettes of the bare thorn trees; only when the shallow breeze-rippled vlei in the depression, glinted and flickered like a crucible, as long shadows grew across the land, and silence fell – and the kudu moved timidly out of the sparse bush, ears flicking and alert, towards the water's edge – did he slip, stealthily from his spare hiding place and, keeping to the shadows and down wind of the kudu and the lioness he had seen waiting in the long grass near the vlei, into the cover of the bush.

His horse whinnied a little way off, and he glanced anxiously at the kudu. Heads raised from the water, they were standing stiffly, ears back, sniffing the air. The lioness, too, looked briefly away from her quarry, then sank deeper into the grass. When the kudu relaxed and bent again to the water, he continued stealthily through the bush.

Another horse whinnied and, this time, it was he who stiffened. The sound had not come from where his own was tethered. It must be one of theirs, but much closer than he had expected. He muttered an oath, hoping grimly that his horse had not given him away.

Still managing to keep downwind of the kudu and lioness, and out of sight of the Boer commando group he knew was

146

tracking him, he skirted through the bush, towards his horse. But he was much too close to them, and could already hear their voices and the cracking of splintering firewood. They seemed to be making camp, and he hoped that meant they were still unaware of him. But he knew that the high price on his head made him a desirable quarry, and that he must get to safer ground as quickly as possible.

Although he managed to reach his horse in silence, the problem now was to lead him away through the dry undergrowth without being heard. Wondering, he looked towards the vlei and, rubbing the horse's nose reassuringly, he raised his field binoculars. The sun was disappearing below the hills, but the veld, glowing bronze through the bush, gave him glimpses of the margins of the burnished copper glinting vlei. The lioness did not keep him waiting.

A few minutes later, she decided that the light was low enough and, slinking from her cover, she streaked across the open ground towards the kudu at the water's edge, curving her approach as they bolted in panic and disarray towards the bush. He took the reins and, in the turmoil of the wild blundering of hooves, and the screeching of a victim being brought down, he stole swiftly away, out of earshot, and into a clump of bush some way off on higher ground.

But, only when the veld was a carpet of rustling darkness, and stars glistened bright in the clear indigo sky, did he unhitch his bedroll and eat some biltong and dry oat biscuits. And, as he drank cold tea from his saddle flask, he pondered with relief the campfire twinkling in the bush below him, and the men who were hunting him.

———————————

The Boers knew who he was, and that he had successfully slipped through their lines many times carrying dispatches from headquarters, and details of Boer movements, to British garrisons in the veld. And they had put a price of £300 on his head.

It had been an arduous week in which he had ridden as far as the Modder River, where General French's army was encamped. From there he had carried dispatches to the garrison commander in Kimberley where a force of four thousand Boers had been laying siege to the town since October.

His body ached from days of riding and nights of sleeping in the veld, but he watched until he was certain that the Boers were resting, before stretching out on his thin bedroll.

Leaning into the forked trunk of a waterberry tree on the edge of his clump of bush, he peered down the slope towards where the Boer patrol had camped overnight. But their fire was long since cold, and only the faint smell of stale wood-smoke, mingled with the cloying scent of kudu dung and marula trees from around the vlei, tickled his nostrils in the otherwise sharp air.

Stars still glinted in the pre-dawn navy sky, and a wraith of mist glowed over the vlei in the stark white moonlight. Around him, the veld was a haze of dull silver. But he watched patiently to ensure that he did not miss their departure. Being down-wind of them, and somewhat higher, there was every chance he would see or hear something, especially since he was fairly sure they were not aware of his presence in their vicinity.

The imperceptible dimming and disappearance of stars above the eastern horizon began long before the sky faded from purple to violet. But, as a dawn breeze rustled the long veld grass, he heard the waking movements of the kudu in the bush below him where they had bolted the evening before in their headlong flight from the lioness.

He found himself wondering about their collective experience and memory. They would soon have to make their way back to drink at the vlei. Would they remember the trauma of the night before, and anticipate another attack? Were they pragmatic about sacrificing one of their number in order to save the herd, or would they reason that, having fed well, the lioness was almost certainly sleeping it off and, with no rival in her territory, they were probably as safe this morning as they would ever be?

His mind refocused suddenly when a thin line of pink streaked across the horizon as if drawn with a fine brush, and a coral wash began drifting across the veld. Within a minute, the great plain was aglow, and the evaporating mist hovered over the vlei like a fluffy pink angora shawl. But, to the west, the low hills were still black, and above them a few stars glistened weakly in the mauve sky.

As the glow crept down the slope in front of him he detected movements on the edge of the bush. He did not use his binoculars for fear of dawn sky lens reflections giving him away, but a neighing horse, and the faint sound of human voices borne on the breeze, told him the Boers were on the move.

Only when they were mounted, and he had noted the direction they were taking, did he break cover and ride in a wide arc to his right so as to keep the bush near the vlei between them and himself. They appeared to be heading west, in much the same direction as he needed to travel himself. He would have to pick up their trails and give them a wide berth.

The mist had cleared by the time he entered the bush near the vlei, and the orange surface glinted and flickered as he moved through the sparse thorn trees. At the water's edge, the kudu drank timidly, their dark brown striped markings ruddy in the dawn, and their long shadows, stretching out to the west along the hoof-trampled margin of sparkling pools, almost reaching the herons and spoonbills wading a little further along.

Even before the sun began to flare over the low mountains to the east, the smell of the arid land and the tang of cactus and eucalyptus in the air told him that, only six weeks into the new century, this would be another scorching day.

Beyond the area of bush he turned a little northwards to move away from the line the Boers had taken, hoping the long grass and the few spare thorn trees would continue to give him cover. Half an hour later he paused and stretched. He should be well clear of them now, and could probably afford a change of direction. For a long time he sat upright in his saddle listening for any sound that might betray the presence of the enemy. Then he flicked the reins and moved forward onto the rutted track that would take him to his local headquarters four hours ride away.

THIRST

Arid, earth-cracked, dust-dry days
of brightly burnished unrelenting skies
that beat their heat upon the unkempt
yellow breeze-rasping tinder grass,
still-born crops and gnarled thorn trees
leafless, screaming silently;
when, just to keep ourselves alive,
we dug for water round the muddy rocks
in the long-since dried-up river bed
with the bones of antelopes who could not dig.

WILD FIRE

No friendly crackling campfire here.
Just the all-consuming ancient roar
of red tsunami, two-trees high and more,
plunging headlong into super-heated
vacuum voids behind the fireball grenades
hurled far ahead through firebreaks and glades,
igniting paths for a sixty mile an hour
crimson tide, a flaming whirlwind raging
through the vaporising vegetation,
a landscape's pyre – once green laid waste.

Early Man, they say, picked up an ember here;
and so, with tinder, first made fire his own.
But then he saw the Tree of Knowledge gone,
and recognised that he and Eve were bare.

7

Elsewhere

ANTIGUA SOUNDS

We thought we'd left the nightly storms behind,
the seething and the sucking in the trees;
the slushing of the rain. That's why we came.
Yet here the bed-time sounds seemed much the same,
except that these, down there beyond the palms,
no more than forty paces
from our simple chalet by the sand,
were of the running tide,
and the soughing of the surf along the strand.

ST JOHNS, ANTIGUA

Sparkling white and vast
the multi-layered P&O confection
looks down with haughty condescension
on multi-coloured modest little buildings
where high street meets the quay and,
palely loitering on less than certain legs,
the wealthy of the world have come to view
the less so of St Johns –
masks of discontented wealth
and targets for the taxi touts.
"You wan' a ride aroun' the island?"
"No thanks, we're not here from the cruise ship –
just simple tourists", we reply.
His eyelids droop – eyes lose their shine.
"OK, man; have a nice day. God bless Antigua".
"OK, man".

Down here, caféd and boutiqued,
the pot-holed gutters, elsewhere running thick
and gravy-grey, are smartly over-planked
as upscale boardwalks for cruise-boat folk
who may not wish to venture further up the road
where life is colourful – and real.

COASTAL HIJAZ

An Ottoman caliphate once
in times when the Turks ruled Islam,
before Lawrence's Arab revolt.

Below arid red-rock mountains
– sun-baked, wind-carved –
stone-strewn, thirst-tortured wadis
anguish beside the sun-bright
cobalt shimmering Red Sea

where ancient coastal camel trails
are printed in the sands of time
– and in the minds of men –

by centuries of camels
of pre-Islamic traders
taking frankincense and myrrh
to Jordan and to Palestine;
and gold, and pearls beyond;

and by the paths the pilgrims rode
from Egypt and Levant
along the coast of Aqaba
to Mecca for the Hajj.

Centuries of camels
plodding down the ages;
plodding out the rhythm
that shaped Islamic verse.

Yet, still, on spice-sharp starlit nights,
by rustling palm-fringed strands,
the phosphorescent surf
froths silver up the sands.

AEGEAN SUNSET
High Summer

There is a glorious moment,
a split second perhaps,
of pure magic
when,
in the white-hot late afternoon sky
a flash of orange
streaks across the horizon,

and the mountains of the Peloponnese,
and the Saronic Islands
 – invisible before in the glare –
are suddenly silhouetted,
sharply etched and jagged,
black against the flare,
before growing purple
in the light of a sea
now become copper,
burning and glinting,
like a lake on fire;

when incandescent
masts and nets and rigging,
spiked filigree in the molten harbour,
sway and creak
in the sunset breeze.

and, when the little Orthodox chapel,
white domed sculpture on the pier,
is bathed in bronze, briefly burnished
by the day's end embers.

AEGEAN SUNSET
Christmas

Leaden clouds, lowering low
over wind-whisked, spray-spitting
green-dark sea;
purple-black island hills recede
to mauve in the mist.

Petulant waves, harbour trapped,
slap seaweed-slimy walls;
boats bob and bump,
squealing and moaning,
protesting their tethered togetherness.

Stay-ropes rattle and hum;
tin bells clink;
frayed-edged flags flutter and splutter
on drunken masts
weaving crazy designs in the slate sky.

Then, through a wind-ripped cloud gash,
gold pours
onto an anthracite island
and fiery-tongued serpents
come writhing and twisting to the shore.

THE JAPANESE LANDINGS
(Aegina, Greece)

In tree-shade near the water-front,
he deftly flips his nosebag up
and grabs another munch of oats.
He hears the bow door scrape, and flicks an ear,
then turns an eye to watch the Japanese
come gliding level-headed down the quay
from Hermes to the harbour-front.

Ahead, demure, the ladies,
mincing neat and parasol-prim
in their broad-brimmed hats,
talk soft, discreet and self-contained.
Behind them, earnestly camcorded men
in casual clothes as smart as bankers' suits,
conviviality constrained,
saunter soberly in step.

An oriental exhibition
come to view the Greeks.

At the harbour-front they turn;
for most, the narrow streets and gift shops
in the town – as if to Aunty Ethel's
in their Sunday best;
for some, the 20 Euro harbour ride
in brightly ribboned jaunty traps,
with garlands, plastic posies, pony bells.

And then…, they vanish for a while
'til, all at once, by e.s.p.,

from side streets, cafés and the water-front,
they reappear and, gliding gift-wrapped,
coalesce along the quay;
no haste or hassle, lates or strays;
an orderly retreat with time to spare,
they float aboard for Poros
and islands further south.

In dappled shade, he hears the bow door clang,
and then the Hermes' parting horn;
he flicks an ear and takes another munch;
he's earned his oats again today.

HARBOUR SOUNDS
(Aegina, Greece)

The clacking hooves and pony bells
distract the conversation on the bench
where two old-timers sort the world
with rasping vocal chords
and cigarette conviction
interspersed with squealing tether ropes
and boats that bump against the quay.

The ferry's anchor rattles
as the gangway grinds the concrete pier
and vehicles rumble off to dock-hands'
calls to keep them straight
and getting shouts and hoots in turn.

That's the coach with tourists
going round the island for an hour
before they re-embark for others
on their one-day islands cruise.

He disagrees, the codger on the bench,
or is it just the scooters he dislikes?
With silencers removed, boy racers
trundle blaring down the harbour front
at 20 miles per hour;
on 50cc Grand Prix mopeds
trying to impress the girls
with sham testosterone,
or think they're at the Isle of Man.

The two old-timers know the tricks,
and wince, and contemplate
their distant misspent youth
while seagulls squawk and fight for crumbs,
then cry and settle grumbling on the masts
and stay-ropes rattling in the breeze.

8

Brief Adventures

A cold shiver down his spine would not describe the sensation. It was more a feeling that his entrails had been spontaneously frozen solid.

Standing only yards away, and a few steps above Brandon on the Piccadilly Circus Eros plinth, bleakly illuminated in the cold fading light of a winter afternoon, was Svetlana Valichkova, one time KGB major, looking directly at him. She had the same expression of ice-cold hatred playing on half-smiling lips that seemed, even in that moment of fear, to be a little less full and alluring than he remembered.

Otherwise she had hardly changed since he had seen her last in 2004 except that, on that occasion, she had been naked in a hotel bedroom in Tbilisi. But this time there was no amusement to be had from the situation, and neither did he see much prospect of an elegant escape.

Back then Svetlana had been sent to Georgia as an *agent provocateur* just after west-leaning Mikheil Saakashvili had been elected president and had begun putting down the separatist movement in South Ossetia. Russian tanks were already assembled in North Ossetia when she arrived in Tbilisi. He, on the other hand, had been posted there to keep an eye on her activities and report on their likelihood of success.

It had not started well for Brandon. But fortunately MI6 had been ahead of the curve and had forewarned him that his businessman cover had probably been compromised and that he should expect an attempt on his life. The message also advised him that Svetlana suffered from an extreme form of arachnophobia, information they had thought might be of assistance to him.

So he had not been altogether surprised when, one evening a day or two later, she had feigned an accidental meeting in the bar of his hotel posing as the foreign correspondent of a Latvian newspaper or that, after a few vodkas, she had become a little flirtatious.

Yet the tingling of excitement and anticipation he felt as he toyed with the realisation that she had been assigned as both his honey-trap and executioner was diminished only by a sense of the tackiness of it all somehow epitomised by the faded Byzantine opulence of the place that had once been a favourite of Stalin's. The threadbare damask upholstery and the grimy chandeliers that excluded more light than they emitted seemed to be a suitable film noir backdrop for their meeting.

And then, looking at her briefly over his glass he had noticed that her skirt appeared to be several inches shorter than when she had first sat down, and that the low light appeared to soften her angular Slavic features. And were her lips really that full, he wondered, or was she pouting?

He just hoped he had not drunk too much vodka.

_____

As the pale early light of dawn had begun to slant through the shutters of his hotel bedroom window, he had been prepared for the end game. Lying on his side, and feigning deep sleep, he had sensed her hand slipping under her pillow beside his head and had contrived a stirring movement as cover to place a convincing replica of a hairy tarantula quivering on his bare shoulder.

Her gasp, part grunt and part stifled scream, had been almost primordial but it had given him the split second he needed to grasp her wrist and wrench the small pistol from her hand. The rest had been easy, if ungainly. Having yanked aside the bedclothes which might have concealed a further weapon, he had dressed and packed with one hand while keeping one eye and the pistol on Svetlana.

Then, in a final gesture, he had picked up her clothes and handbag from a chair and dropped them casually into his valise, snapping it shut with theatrical finality. She had stared in anguish as the implications of his action dawned on her, and it was then that he had seen the half smile of cold vengeful hatred.

"I will get you for this", she had snarled.

"Why so angry, my dear?" he had asked sweetly. "Last night's encounter was entirely your idea. I have done you no harm and, once I have left, you will be free to leave whenever you like."

After ripping the telephone cable from the wall, and ensuring that she had no other means of electronic communication, he had opened the bedroom door and, while stepping out into the corridor, he had tossed the tarantula onto the bed beside her. This time she had screamed aloud.

It may all have been rather amusing, but Brandon knew very well at the time that her parting words had been no idle threat and that now, here in Piccadilly Circus, the cards were in her favour.

As her hand slipped into her shoulder bag he stepped behind a large American tourist, and then quickly behind the man's female companion. Looking over the woman's shoulder he realised that Svetlana had vanished – but there was no doubt she was there watching him from somewhere nearby among the other tourists.

He continued stepping backwards, moving quickly from behind one person to another, working his way towards the Lower Regent Street side of Piccadilly Circus.

'Pity about the lips', he thought wryly as he dodged through the traffic and into Glasshouse Street a few moments later. 'I could have died more happily if they had been a little fuller.' He knew she would not be far behind him so he covered the short distance to Air Street very quickly where turning left brought him back into Lower Regent Street. Squinting left as he emerged into the last rays of the sun he spotted her entering Glasshouse Street a short distance away.

When he caught up with her in an almost dark alley she was peering between some large pungent waste bins at the rear of an Indian restaurant, a pistol in her hand. Sliding along a shadowed wall towards the bins he felt grateful he had discarded them earlier as a possible hiding place. Then he stepped out quietly behind her and grabbed her right wrist. The pistol dropped into a half open bin.

"Hello Svetlana", he said. "What's a nice girl like you doing in a place like this?"

STAKE-OUT

For me night is the best time for walking. Why? Because it's when I get to think more clearly about the hoodlums and misfits I spend my days trying to nail – mostly for well-heeled hoods who want to find some broad who's gone missing, usually because she's decided to go missing.

But even the daytime stuff is dark – low life in the shadows. So night walking is good for reflection. The way I see it is, if you take the light out of the question, it's easier to figure out what's happening in the dark.

Now, take that punk over there – the one leaning against the lamp post with a broken light above him. What's he doing with his hat pulled down over his eyes, his collar turned up, cigarette dangling from the corner of his mouth? He's trying to look like a regular gumshoe. Except that he aint. Why not? Because he used to be a regular cop – until they busted him. Now he's just a nickel-and-dime grifter casing the big place opposite – the one with the fancy gates – because a dame called Loretta got herself mixed up with Joe Fenetti, the capo of a local outfit who lives there.

So I'm here watching this two-bit louse-bag. Been looking for him for six years – and that's a lotta rye under the Brooklyn Bridge – since we were both busted from the NYPD for unprofessional conduct, when he was my sergeant and messed up a night stake-out job. Being bright isn't his strong suit – maybe he was never dealt one – a bit of a schmuck. I stick some gum in my mouth.

Now, watching him from the shadows in this dark alley, I get the same feeling I had back then. We was in a sleaze-bag house on Krenshaw in a tough Bronx neighbourhood and, me, I was looking out an upstairs window at the house opposite.

Somethin' about the place didn't smell right. And how could the sergeant identify it so easily in the dark from a back service alley? He had a bad fit of coughing at the briefing so that I, for sure, and probably himself also, couldn't hear the address of the joint. Plus, why was it unoccupied? But, hey, I am only a rookie detective, so what the hell would I know?

But I go on wondering as I set up the tripod and camera behind the window overlooking the street. Then I ease it up to the crack between the threadbare velvet curtains and check out the house on the other side through my binoculars.

"Goin' for a leak," says my colleague, and he disappears through the bedroom and closes the door behind him.

That worries me too. Why did he close the door, and why am I hearing running water, and not a flushing toilet? Maybe to muffle the sound of his voice? 'Hey, man, leave it', I tell myself, and I take a slug from my hip flask.

But it don't help me none, so I open the bedroom door and sashay into the hall outside. I can hear his voice gravelling above the running faucet in the bathroom. I can't hear what he is saying but I figure he must be speaking to someone on the metal fire escape outside the bathroom window.

Then a floor board creaks under my foot – and he stops talking. I hear him move and I sneak quickly back into the bedroom – but I leave the door partly open behind me.

By the time he comes back I'm squinting through the camera lens at the house opposite. I hear him open a brief case and the rustle of papers as he checks the case notes. Then he opens one of the bags of bagels and schmear we picked up on the way, and I hear him munching.

"Didya open the bedroom door while I was in the john?" he asks casually.

"Yes, Sarge", I reply easily, pretending to be busy with my work. "Thought I heard a noise downstairs, and went to check."

"Sure", he says, but I can tell he doesn't believe me.

Then, I see the problem. Although I missed the address at the briefing, I remembered from the photographs that the street door of the target house had clear glass in the fanlight. But this one has coloured glass. So I turn the binoculars to scan the rest of the street and I see the crooked fire hydrant I also remember from the photographs – along ways further down. And that's when it smacks me right between the eyes – we are staking out the wrong house! This whole damn thing is beginning to stink like rotten fish in a heated janitor's closet.

"Hey, Sarge, there's something wrong here", I say – then realise I shoulda kept my trap shut.

The munching stops, and the papers go quiet. I can feel his eyes on my back. My neck tingles as I continue scanning the house down the street. He knows I've sussed it. Then I hear his casual jacket whisper as he gets up from the chair where he's been reading, and I feel the breeze he makes as he arrives close behind me.....and I smell his garlic breath.

Self-preservation kicks in – fast. I step quickly to one side, then turn and slam my binoculars into his temple. He drops like a felled bull, and a pistol falls from his hand onto the floor. The sergeant is so full of hot air you could fly a balloon with it, but that didn't fool Internal Affairs none. They put the squeeze on him and pretty soon he sings. So they decide he's a two-timing bent cop who gave the mob a free ride on some bootlegged booze operation in the house we shoulda been watching. He gets five in the can. But they reckon I'm guilty also – of assaulting a fellow officer. Who knows, maybe they thought I was in on the booze job.

Unreasonable? Yeah, I guess I thought so, which is why I am here watching that louse over there. And it's why I spit my gum on the ground, then lift my rifle and focus the night vision sight. And it's why I'm thinking they'll guess the shot was fired by some other small time creep, like himself, operating in life's shadows, maybe with a score to settle.

And, if that's what they think, I guess they'll be right.

S usan Campbell backed her mobile library van gingerly into the passage between the newsagents and the ironmongers. A little farther back, the passage opened out into the late Joe Baxter's motor repair workshop, but she stopped just short of the vehicle inspection pit, its tarred cover-boards barely distinguishable from the surrounding tarmac.

The forward part of the vehicle could be seen easily in the High Street, so she hoped her customers would spot her despite the unfamiliar location. She looked down towards the lay-by at the other end and, sure enough, two or three regulars, who had been waiting there, were already ambling towards her.

"Why the new spot?" asked Anne Trowbridge as she stepped aboard.

"Well, the shopkeepers down there have been muttering that I obstruct their delivery vehicles. So I hoped, with Joe Baxter having passed away, that no one would object to my obstructing his yard for an hour or so."

"No, I'm sure it's okay," Bill Davies interjected from behind. "But it's funny, though, you choosing a place of recent local fame."

"Fame? Why?"

"Stolen goods," he replied conspiratorially. "Don't you remember the burglary up at the church last year – shortly before Joe Baxter died?"

"Oh, yes; the sculpture?"

"Early Medieval stone carving actually. Very rare. Been in the church for centuries."

"But what's that got to do with Joe's yard?"

"Well, you see; the couple in the flat above the newsagents, were disturbed that night, and saw two men dragging something heavy in here on a trailer shortly after the vicar phoned the police to report a similar trailer being dragged out of the churchyard. The police were here in no time. They set up road blocks, searched the workshop, but found nothing. But they're convinced it's still somewhere nearby; too heavy to move very far, you see. So they're still watching the yard …"

His voice tailed off when he noticed Anne Trowbridge staring absently towards the rear.

"The inside of your van looks shorter," she remarked.

"Yes, it's the children's section. Some of the shelves got damaged, so they screened off the last three feet or so pending repairs. But there are some children's books in the miscellaneous section," she added helpfully.

"No, that's fine, thanks. My son doesn't want one this week."

Anne Trowbridge looked up from her book in Alice Pertwee's teashop, disturbed by the library van scraping over a road hump outside in the High Street. "That's unusual," she thought. "The rear end looks very low." Then, across the road, she noticed James Weaver, the antiquarian bookseller, pause in the passage beside the ironmongers. He turned in towards the yard, and then trod his heel a few times around the edge of the inspection pit.

THE HANDOVER

*A*lthough they were expecting the telephone to ring at precisely 11.00am, both men jumped when it did. The man behind the desk moved involuntarily towards the phone, then hesitated, his hand hovering over the insistent instrument. The man across the desk, who was wearing headphones, tightened his lips and nodded grimly. The first man picked up the handset. His mouth was dry, and he had to moisten his lips before answering.

"Hello? Yes, this is Charles Thompson. Yes, I have the money as we agreed."

The man with the headphones motioned him to keep talking for as long as possible.

"Yes, but you'll have to allow me to get things straight, or we'll both suffer if the arrangements are botched … Now look here! I want my wife back, and I know damn well that if I don't do precisely what you want … OK, OK, get on with it then …

"Yeees, I've got that. Gatwick Airport, South Terminal, International Arrivals Meeting Point. Café Nero, beside the meeting point; the nearest table to the main concourse. 3.30pm. Today? That's very tight. OK, if I leave now, I might just about make it.

"Well, I'm medium height, mid forties, dark hair, grey at the temples …"

Above the voice on the telephone he heard articulated hisses coming from the headphones opposite him, and he saw the

other man's features relax. His people outside must have got a "fix" on the incoming phone call. He continued more slowly …
"… dark blue suit, red tie and white pocket handkerchief …"

As he spoke he noticed the face opposite change again, to perplexity, and then concern.

"… The briefcase? Well, it's light brown pigskin with brass fittings and … OK, OK, I'm leaving." He put the phone down.

As he got up, the other man yanked his headphones off, and demanded curtly,

"What the hell was all that about a blue suit? You haven't got time to change!"

"Come on, George, you must have realised that I was describing you!"

"What …?"

"Don't let's mess about, George. There isn't time. I'm leaving Helen in your capable hands. We both know you've been seeing each other for most of the past year and, now, as far as I'm concerned, she's all yours. You have a fix on the call, and I'm sure that, with your resources, you can follow the man who picks up the briefcase at Gatwick. That's it over there, by the way – but it's empty. You might even find a location tracking bug to put inside. Now, if you'll excuse me, I have a golf match at 1.30. I should be somewhere near the 12th green when your man picks up the briefcase."

THE HANDBAG

Christine read the anonymous letter with horror, instantly recalling the moment she'd hit the fourth form boy when he'd tried to steal the girls' hockey ball. She'd realised at the time that she'd crossed the line. But the girls had seemed to support her, and she'd returned to the coaching practice with the ball and a sigh of relief.

Now, one of them, perhaps one who hadn't been picked for the team, had decided to make an issue of it. But the hockey team wasn't what the letter was about – it was about £1000 in used banknotes or the risk of suspension and disciplinary action. She was damned if she did, and damned if she didn't. And it was clear that the amount had been carefully set so as make it the more attractive alternative.

The letter, the output of an untraceable home printer, told her to go to the ladies' toilet on the first floor of Hamiltons Department Store at 9.10 precisely on Saturday morning where, at the far right-hand side of the vanity shelf, she would find a pink lipstick case with further instructions.

Christine reflected on the level of forethought involved with a degree of admiration. This helped to steady her nerves and, in turn, encourage her to engage intellectually with her blackmailer.

The pick-up time had also been well chosen. Hamiltons was still relatively quiet at 9.10, and the toilets even more so. In fact, they seemed to be completely empty as Christine picked up the lipstick case. But she wondered about the end closet which was very slightly open. As she approached it, the door snapped shut.

She turned aside to one of the other cubicles and, as she examined the instructions, heard footsteps leaving the toilet. Printed in small type on narrow strips of thin paper, rolled up inside the scratched pink lipstick case, the instructions were very specific.

She was to buy a particular Gucci handbag from the leathergoods department, put the money in a plain envelope in an inside pocket together with the sales receipt for the bag, and return to the toilets at exactly 10.45. There she was to place the handbag on the floor of the end cubicle partially under the partition shared with the adjoining cubicle. Then she was to go directly up to the café on the second floor, order a cappuccino immediately, another at 11.10, and keep both receipts. If she failed to fulfill any detail of the instructions, the deal would be off.

Christine puzzled for a moment over the café part of the arrangements and then, with a wry smile, realised that it was to ensure she would be out of the way, and out of sight, while the girl retrieved the handbag and left the store.

She carried out the instructions to the letter, and more, noting also the occupied toilet second from the end. But she decided to have her cappuccino in a different café – the one across the pedestrian broadwalk from the store's main entrance where, she reckoned, she may only need to buy one cup.

At 11.02 she saw Mavis saunter out of the store, a self-satisfied smirk on her face, a smart Gucci bag on her shoulder – and a security guard on her heels. Once clear of the door, the guard took her by the elbow and escorted her back inside.

Christine took another sip of her coffee, sat back, and smiled her own smile of satisfaction. She wondered how Mavis would explain the stolen gold bracelet in the semi-secret inner pocket, still attached to the electronic tag which had alerted the security people. And she would also have difficulty explaining the fifty £20 notes in the Barclays wrapper, especially when it was discovered that the serial numbers had been recorded as being paid out that very morning – to someone else.

But, she supposed, the scratched pink lipstick case would seem innocent enough – unless, that is, someone looked inside!

"Hi! I'm the postmistress. Special delivery." She chuckled as she handed me a small Christmas stocking. "To be picked up on 29th December – so you can't open it! And they said you got something for me."

Standing there on my doorstep in motorcycle leathers in a light Christmas Eve snowfall, her slim form in a truculent attitude, she looked anything but a postmistress. Her helmet and the darkness obscured her face but, through the visor, the porch light picked out eyes that were bright and alert, even rebellious.

"Thanks – yes I have something for you. Just a minute." I withdrew to the hall-stand behind me, placed the stocking on the brass letter tray and returned with the small brown envelope which had been left with me for collection. She took it and examined it briefly before looking up at me suspiciously.

"What's this?" she snapped.
"I've no, idea. Johnny 'phoned half an hour ago, and asked me to add that note to the envelope."
She looked again at the words I had written, 'emailvirus@ mole.hill', before looking up again. Her bright eyes were hard.
"Cheers, mate; Happy Christmas," she said brusquely. Then she turned and marched down the snow-covered path to the powerful motorbike at the kerb outside. "Thanks, and the same to you – mate," I murmured absentmindedly as she thundered up the slushy hill on her big beast. "But I wonder what you're up to."

I was still wondering ten minutes later, as I settled into an armchair by the fire in my study with a mince pie and mulled wine. I decided I needed to analyse the thing from the beginning, four years ago.

A man from the Language Translation Centre had come to see me after I had replied to an ad in the South London Advertiser for freelance translators. I had been surprised to be offered sixty days' work per year at premium rates in exchange for occasionally acting as a post box for small packages which would be dropped and collected. Once a month at most, he had said. Security services, he had hinted. I wasn't bothered. I needed the work.

It had been an undemanding and profitable arrangement. But, this time was different. As always, Johnny had phoned to mention the impending envelope which had duly arrived by hand a day or two later – but badly sealed. It had opened easily and, inside, I had found two theatre tickets for "The Magic Roundabout" at 'The Theatre Royal', Halliday Road, Streatham, on 2nd January.

Then, this evening, shortly before the arrival of 'the postmistress', Johnny had 'phoned again. He had sounded tense, and told me to write on the envelope the words, 'emailvirus@mole.hill.' Nothing like that had happened before. Something was amiss, and 'the postmistress's' reaction had confirmed it.

I reached for the Yellow Pages. There was no 'Theatre Royal' in Streatham. My mind drifted back to my days at MI5. Language translation – not 'active' – but the thinking rubs off. What were these people up to, and what had worried them?

The mental activity froze as a stray thought struggled for attention. Hadn't there been a number of daring Post Office robberies in South London in the past few years? I opened the Yellow Pages again. There was a Royal Mail depot in Halliday Road, Streatham, and the London Streetfinder showed it to be on a roundabout! I picked up the 'phone and dialled a secure line.

I was working on a translation on 3rd January when the telephone rang. It was my old colleague from MI5.

"I thought you'd retired," he said. "How did you get onto this Royal Mail thing?"

"Oh, just a little accidental intelligence, plus some reactivated grey cells."

"Well, the Serious Crime Squad got them last night, you know. But nearly missed the get-away van with the crazy driver – a woman known as 'the postmistress'. Master-minded by an ex MI5 operative; calls himself 'Johnny'; tried to run villains in discrete cells using security service methods."

"I'm glad I was of help."

"Well, actually, it wasn't only you. You provided the date, but the Met had their suspicions too; in fact they had a mole in the depot by the name of Hill."

"Ah! The emailvirus@mole.hill. I didn't think of that."

"What was that?"

"Nothing. Just eating a mince pie," I said. "By the way, I don't suppose you need any freelance translaters, do you?"

I looked at the woman across the table from me and tried to recognise the girl of fifteen I had last seen thirty-six years before. There were the blue eyes and the fair hair, but I didn't think I could expect much more after all that time. I tried to get a glimpse of her right hand, but she seemed fussily anxious and kept it out of sight fiddling with her handbag and her table napkin.

"I hope you don't mind having afternoon tea with your uncle," I enquired innocently. "That's assuming you even recognise me after all these years."

"Yes, I recognise you, but it's difficult. You were away a lot when I was growing up."

I noticed the curious blend of hesitant Roedean English with a kind of Slavic Nordic. An understandable mixture in the circumstances, I thought.

"But, I have to ask why this meeting is necessary," she continued. "The bank and the solicitors were satisfied with the evidence of my identification, so why can't they just give me access to my inheritance? And what have you to do with my business anyway?"

"Yes, I can understand your frustration, but I am sure you can see that 'your' business is quite complicated. You are kidnapped in Lithuania during a school Baltic cruise, and your parents are killed in a plane crash on the way out there to see the police about the ransom demand. You are orphaned and then lost to the world. I am abroad at the time, and your parents' considerable estate is put in trust for you with two trustees. The trail goes cold, and the courts make you my ward in absentia. Hence my interest in you; apart from being your uncle, of course. And then, thirty-six years later, soon after the last trustee dies, you turn up having found your way from a remote convent in the mountains in the far north of Lithuania."

"Yes, I know how it sounds, but it's not as complicated as that. I was taken there soon after the plane crash by men who said my father was a British spy and that I needed protection from the KGB. This was 1973 remember. So I was stuck there for all that time, a prisoner near the Latvian border, in a convent with a very strict rule where nobody knew what was happening outside. It was only recently that things relaxed and I heard someone say my name in a BBC World Service programme. But, what matters is, I still have my original passport, and the convent has certified that I was there all the time. What more can anyone want?"

Not much, I had to admit to myself, but it worried me that, while the convent's letter certified that Rebecca Thornton had been with them for thirty-six years, there seemed to be no direct link between that person and the one sitting in front of me. So I continued trying to get a look at her right hand and the permanently deformed middle finger, the result of a riding accident in a school gymkhana. Sooner or later she would have to drink her tea.

I raised my own cup as casually as I could. A moment later she did the same, and there it was – a crooked middle finger hooked around the side of the cup like a talon. I breathed a sigh of relief. It was almost as good as a birthmark.

"You're quite right," I replied cheerfully. "I don't think anything else is wanted."

She relaxed as well, and smiled for the first time as she raised her napkin. As she dabbed her lips I noticed that the middle finger of her right hand was as straight as all the others.

I think it was the sheer dereliction of the place, the apparent lack of a moderating human presence, rather than the moisture-laden late September afternoon, that made me feel suddenly cold.

The privet hedge was bedraggled, dishevelled and overgrown, uneven and leaning precariously under the weight of its own off-balance obesity. I wondered if it was the right house. But it was. Number forty six. The cheap aluminium numerals on the rotting wooden gatepost said so even though they were oddly aligned with the six much lower than the four.

The other gatepost had sagged inwards so that the bottom outside corner of the slightly ajar rusted wrought-iron gate was resting jammed on the ground. Curved scrape marks gouged into the earth on the other side were gritty testimony to the resistance it would offer to being opened. I had to lift both gate and post before I could pass through.

Beyond, the path to the front door was discernible only as a change of texture in the eighteen inch high wild grass that had taken over the whole front garden. Beneath my feet as I moved forward I noticed, largely hidden by the grass, a few broken paving slabs randomly arranged here and there. Crazy paving suddenly took on a new meaning. I shivered again and pulled my jacket collar closer to my neck. To my right a sickly sweet smell told me that the partially flattened area of grass below the apple tree was not some kind of crop circle, but the rotting remains of uncollected windfalls.

Despite the lateness of the afternoon no lights were on that I could see behind the unlined curtains that hung unevenly behind the grimy windows. But a dim glow behind the cracked fanlight glass over the front door, where once a pretty stained glass art deco sunburst design would have welcomed visitors, suggested the possibility of a human presence within.

The peeling brown door was devoid of a means of announcing my arrival. Only a small tarnished plate in the centre gave a hint of there having once been a proud fluted brass knocker. The springless lightweight aluminium letter plate squeaked as I pushed it inwards and clinked without gravitas as it fell back. The activity elicited no response that I could detect, so I crouched down and, opening the plate again, peered into the dank and bare floor-boarded gloom beyond.

A faint scraping sound focused my attention as the barrel of a shiny automatic pistol was thrust forward through the opening coming to rest just short of my eyes. In the dark void of the gun's muzzle I saw an image of a small screw hole in a rotting gatepost just to the right of the apex of an aluminium numeral 'four'. Of course, I thought. The nine was now hanging upside down from its bottom screw. This was not the right house!

9

Whimsical Views

ART CRITIQUE
A report in the Accringham Echo by the paper's fine art correspondent

"The Town Hall's banqueting room glittered radiantly on Saturday evening on the occasion of a rare gala event, attended by the Mayor in full regalia, the Town Council, the Trustees of the Accringham Art Gallery, and most of the town's movers and shakers. Champagne in crystal goblets competed for brilliance with sparkling ladies and newly cleaned chandeliers; and white-gloved waiters in evening dress served gourmet crudités on Spode china plates emblazoned with the Council's coat of arms.

The occasion was to celebrate the acquisition of an important piece of modern sculpture for the Art Gallery. In due course it will be exhibited in a room of its own, but for the occasion it had pride of place in the centre of the banqueting room where it enjoyed the appreciation of the cognoscenti who examined it with rapt attention, murmuring approvingly.

The piece can be described fairly easily. Sitting on a pedestal about three feet high, there is a base comprising two army-issue blankets each neatly folded to a square of about two feet by two feet, and placed one on top of the other. Above that are clay bricks in three layers of diminishing sizes, so forming a stepped pyramid.

After speeches of welcome by the Mayor and the Chairman of the Trustees of the Art Gallery, the latter introduced the evening's guest of honour, the well-known fine art critic, Byron Tulle who had come from London in order to give an appreciation of the sculpture. After thanking his hosts, he went on to say:

'Ladies and Gentlemen, I stand here tonight a man moved to the point of extremis; emotionally and intellectually humbled by the

profundity of this work on which, with both joy and trepidation, I will attempt to comment.

I call it a "work" because, in the richness of its multi-layered esotericism, it transcends prosaic labels like sculpture or art. Existentially, this piece goes to the very heart of being and the meaning of being in a concrete and deterministic way that cannot avoid limiting or conditioning our choice.

Here the folded blankets (note that there are two – alluding to the eternal duality of the cosmos (to which the Yin-Yang also speaks) refers to the three-dimensional weft and warp of unrealised possibilities, opposing any concept that views man as the manifestation of an absolute or infinite substance, or Husserl's explicit espousal of the ontological priority of possibility over reality, possibility here not in the purely logical sense of the absence of contradiction, but in the sense of traditional metaphysics as potentially constrained to become reality.

The bricks by contrast allude to a constructivist quality of reality which denies mass as a plastic element and volume as an expression of space. On the other hand, they continue the metaphor of layers, except that here they are individuated, unconnected, with no binding element as in the weft and warp below since, as in Dadaism, they represent a nihilistic, anti-aesthetic and anti-rationalistic critique of society – indeed an attack on formal artistic conventions and a rejection of bourgeois values.

But, in this, they also refer back to the blankets, brilliantly completing the circle and providing a subtle cohesion and ontological unity to the piece, serving the same function as that of a dream, in that it frees the individual from the paralysing emotional scruples of self-abnegation, and affirms the priority of possibility over reality.'

The strength of the prolonged applause from the discerning audience caused the chandeliers to tinkle and sparkle their parallel approval."

*T*he silver Rolls Royce turned left off the High Street of the Sussex market town and into Plain Street, a time-frozen but unremarkable road of traditional artisan shops. Even as late as the mid-1960s this aptly named side street had not changed much since the Second World War.

A casual passer-by might have caught a glimpse of stocky old Fred Beesley, the butcher, through the curtain of half-carcasses, fully feathered game birds and strings of sausages hanging inside his shop window as he separated pork chops on a massive chopping board behind the old marble-topped counter.

And Edwards Electrical to the left of Beesley's still displayed a few pre-war light-fittings beside a selection of 'modern' shades and lamp bases jumbled together in the front window with a couple of kettles, drums of electrical cable and hand-wound cards of fuse wire. At a large wooden desk at the rear Joe Edwards was repairing an electric toaster. He paused and looked up briefly, noticing the Rolls Royce passing his shop front.

If you were to have partially closed your eyes to exclude the bright sunlight and soften the colours you might have been looking at a photographic print from the 1930s. Except, that is, for the shining Rolls Royce Silver Ghost parked outside the ironmongers just beyond the barbers – and the fur-coated lady being helped out by her chauffeur.

———————

Inside, behind the sawdust covered wooden counter, khaki-coated Selwyn Jones almost jumped to attention when the little Victorian bell tinkled and the imposing lady stepped in through the Art Deco glass shop door. She paused briefly, her natural authority wavering in the unfamiliar environment as she looked with bewilderment at the display rack of sledge hammers, chisels and large coarse-toothed wood saws. Then she sniffed with distaste as her nostrils sampled the blend of paint, parafin and linseed oil.

As she turned away from the door, Jones could see the Rolls Royce parked outside, guarded by its almost matching grey-uniformed chauffeur, his peaked cap under his arm, grey suede gauntlets in one hand and gleaming boots at attention.

"Can I be of assistance, madam?"

"A screw, if you please," she replied, her hauteur recovered.

"A screw, madam?"

"I believe that is what I said!"

"Yes madam, but just one screw?"

"Precisely! This is an ironmongers, is it not?"

"Indeed it is, madam."

"And is it not usual for ironmongers to sell screws?"

"Very much so, madam, and we have a comprehensive range."

"Good! Then I would be obliged if you would please sell me one."

"Of course, madam, if madam would advise me as to the kind of screw she requires."

"My man, I do not intend to be drawn into a discussion on the subject of screws. I require merely that you sell me one."

"Very well, madam", he replied turning to withdraw a small box from the neatly packed shelves behind him. "Here is a box of five-inch sheradised steel counter-sinking wood-screws with Phillips heads. Would one of these be satisfactory, perhaps?"

"Of course not. They're much too big!"

"If madam would perhaps tell me the purpose for which the screw is required, I might be able to offer more assistance."

"Very well, if you insist on prying, it is to repair the tool box for my motorcar."

"The wooden tool box on the running-board of the car outside, madam?"

"Yes."

"Might I ask your chauffeur to show it to me so that I can inspect the damage?"

"No, you may not. I will ask him to bring it in myself."

"Presumably madam is referring to the clasp to the box?"

"Quite! I require a screw to repair the clasp."

"But, madam, the clasp is broken and cannot be repaired, least of all with a screw. On the other hand, I can offer madam a replacement brass clasp. Not exactly the same design, but neat and suitable nevertheless. Would that be of assistance?"

"Of course, man. That is why I am here!"

"Very good, madam. And I presume that madam will require suitable screws with which to secure the clasp?

"Naturally!"

"I would suggest four half-inch brass number fives with domed heads. And, incidentally, madam, I see that there is some damage to the joint at the corner of the lid. Would madam perhaps like me to repair that at the same time?"

She turned to her chauffeur for confirmation. He nodded obsequiously.

"Very well. What do you suggest?"

"A screw, madam."

"What kind of screw exactly?"

"A three-quarter inch number 6 counter-sinking flat-headed brass screw. With our compliments, madam. One loose screw!"

S hafts of slanting sun, slicing through the stately potted palms and between the tall bell-topped Egyptian columns, shimmered on the sequinned dresses of the Nefertiti Palm Court String Quartet as they swayed languidly to their own soft strains of 'Smoke Gets in Your Eyes'. Waitresses, demure in black and white, flitted between sun-spattered, white-clothed tables, silent on the thick Egyptian carpet which also muffled the clink of china and the already low tones of the voices.

Some way off, discreetly by the large papyrus-design glass doors, the brushed and brilliantined hair of the morning-suited manager flashed in the low sunlight as he bowed when the overdressed woman with two furtive-looking pre-teen boys in school uniforms entered the Palm Court of the Hotel Majestic. Her colourful hat wobbled as she tossed her head. Then she sniffed, standing truculently, one hand on her hip, feet apart.

The manager eyed the trio with carefully concealed genteel disaproval.

"Good afternoon, madam. May I be of assistance?"

"Yeh!", she snapped, "Me an' my boys, come 'ere for the Christmas afternoon tea."

"Of course, madam."

As he straightened, the manager extended a nonchalant arm and flicked the fingers of his white gloved hand. Almost instantly, the waitress he had seen without looking, presented herself before the new arrivals.

"Take madam and these young …", he paused for further appraisal of the boys as the word "gentlemen" wedged in his throat, "… to a table for four near the verandah." His reverential tone, obsequious smile and the inclination of his head, did not entirely disguise the curl in his lip as he spoke.

Dismissing the waitress with a gesture of disdain and disapproval, the woman stomped off inelegantly – her high-heeled, pigeon-toed gait reminiscent of Dick Emery in drag – towards a table beside the string quartet, the boys trailing sullenly behind her.

Once seated she laid aside her chartreuse synthetic feather boa and withdrew the hatpin that partially secured a confection of orange and violet organza and net but which was not quite able to support the large puce artificial rose drooping on one side. The hat removed, she ostentatiously patted her newly rinsed hair which might have reminded a casual viewer of over-pink candyfloss twirled into an uncertain beehive shape with sticky wisps top and bottom.

The prim and pretty waitress waited just long enough for the patrons to settle before handing them their afternoon tea menus and withdrawing.

Then, with ash curling off the end of the gold-tipped Russian cigarette hanging in her loose mouth, she picked her nose, while the boys, still wearing their school caps, slobbered over their menus. The elegant waitress reappeared and hovered discreetly.

"… and tea for madam?" she asked after the pastries had been ordered.

"Yeh," rasped 'madam' curtly through kippered vocal chords. The cigarette wobbled as she spoke, and the ash dropped onto the white table cloth.

"Assam or Ceylon?"

"Nah! Incha got any … watcha call it … Shiplapsingsong?"

"Lapsang souchong? Yes madam."

All three had obviously succeeded in identifying the most exotic concoctions in the pastrycook's exuberant repertoire; but neither boy was prepared to begin eating first. Each tried to goad the other into starting by making lip-smacking noises, until one put his tongue a little too close to the other's oozing Pavlova, and had his face driven smartly down into its voluptuous softness.

One of the violins squawked as the mother jumped up and, shouting obscenities at the villain, hit him with her hat. The flimsy assembly disintegrated into the other boy's cream-smothered chocolate-and-toffee gateau, and a large puce rose settled decorously into his malted fudge milkshake.

A startled waitress appeared, and enquired if she could help.

"Bugger orf, you stupid bitch!", shrieked the woman. "Can'tcha bleedin' well see I'm busy?"

The Nefertiti String Quartet wavered and trailed off discordantly, then regained its composure and, sequins sparkling rhythmically in the sunlight, continued playing, perhaps a little too enthusiastically, 'You're the Cream in my Coffee' while, a little way off, the manager, his white-gloved hands knotted into writhing balls, squirmed a very cultured squirm.

THE RENOIR EXHIBITION
She finds herself beside him looking at the same painting
(Dance at Bougival)

He: Don't you think it's fun to speculate?

She: On what?

He: Body language for instance.

She: Whose body language?

He: The figures in the painting.

She: And what do you deduce from theirs?

He: See how he leans towards her holding her firmly to him with his arm around her waist while staring intently into her face.

She: Well?

He: Well, don't you see the way she in turn leans away from him, her face turned away from his, eyes cast down?

Is there some resistance on her part do you think?

She: Okay, but maybe she's just demure.

After all she's got her hand around his neck.

He: So, what d'you think is on her mind?

She: Maybe he's invited her to slip away to a nearby café for a drink.

He: Yes …, then perhaps he's pressing her for an answer, staring at her, trying to persuade her.

What do you think she'll say?

She: Well, I'm not so sure that's what he's asked her.

He: But if he had?

She: If he had what?

He: Asked her for a drink.

She: I believe I might.

He: Really?

She: Really what?

He: Really agree to have a drink.

She: With him?

He: No, with me.

She: Okay.

"Good evening. Interesting piece, isn't it?"

The earnest and animated conversation stopped dead, and all nine establishment art critics, the whole proprietorial circle around the newly acquired sculpture – a kind of three-dimensional montage – turned, champagne glasses in their hands, and stared at me.

Their expressions were not friendly – something like the silent interrogation of airport security guards. And, like security guards, the uniformity of the dress of the six men, black ties and dinner jackets, reinforced the impression of their ranks massed to repel boarders.

Sebastian St Germain, probably the most eminent among them, was the first to speak.

"I should have thought 'a work of genius' might have been more apposite a characterisation than 'interesting'."

"Praise indeed!", I replied, trying to disguise the confrontational response I felt.

"Then you mustn't have heard my unveiling speech half an hour ago", he surmised acidly.

"No, I'm afraid I missed it. I was busy elsewhere in the gallery."

"Ah! So you are not an art critic then?", asked Arabella Reislip-Green, art editor on one of the broadsheets. The relief she derived from her deduction was obvious. Not being one of them I no longer merited the normal courtesies accorded to their fraternity.

"No, I am a conservator. I took delivery of this piece recently on behalf of the gallery when it was bought for a controversially high price – the acquisition we are all celebrating tonight."

"Oh, I see. You are a … ah, technician." Ms Reislip-Green moved in to reinforce my exclusion.

"Actually, I am a scientist so that 'technologist' would be more accurate. Dr John Howard, Head of Conservation here at the Gilbankian Museum of Modern Art. And, since our definitions don't seem to coincide entirely, perhaps you could explain to me why you think it is a work of genius – in particular, the red knickers poking out from the folded copy of the Financial Times?"

The creators and custodians of the definitions of 'art' looked at me with undisguised pity.

"Scarlet, actually." Sebastian St Germain corrected me. "Scarlet knickers in the folds of the Financial Times …"

"… No doubt symbolising the prostitution of the banking and financial services establishment", I interrupted. "Yes, I think that's fairly obvious. But what about the broken china piggy-bank?"

"Also self-evident I should have thought", he replied. "Empty, of course. Our money – raided and lost by cash-intoxicated dealers."

"I presume the Wells Fargo reward poster …"

"… A replica from 1883", he interrupted. "The reward was offered for the apprehension of the robbers who stole a million dollars in Government Bonds from a Wells Fargo stage coach. A double-edged reference to the Government bail-out of our banks and the rewards given to irresponsible bank executives."

"And, I suppose the charred end of the Financial Times represents the destruction caused by the economic collapse?"

"Precisely!"

"But what about the bird in the ashes?"
Arabella Reislip-Green intervened. "As you will observe on closer inspection, 'the bird' is a Phoenix with a broken wing, signifying that it will not rise from the ashes. We will not again be consumed by the flames of avarice and self-indulgence."

"Do you believe that?"

"Yes, indeed I do", she replied. "I believe the days of junkets and gravy trains are over."

"Don't you think you're under-estimating the capacity of human nature to forget all this trauma and return to old habits?"

"No I don't at all."

"But, aren't we doing that right now? Isn't this event a junket? Nine well known and highly respected pundits of the art world drinking champagne while pontificating about the merits of a piece of over-priced second-rate art in arcane and obscure terms not unlike those used by City whizz-kids to describe highly suspect financial products? In fact don't you think that this work is actually little more than an easily-decipherable three-dimensional version of a cartoon of the kind one might expect to find in the Sunday broadsheets?"

"Well! That's a bit rich coming …"

"Coming from a technician? But isn't that exactly the merit of it? Emblematic of the man in the street's disaffection with the gobbledygook of the City traders – and other so-called specialists. By the way, are any of you gentlemen wearing red – I'm sorry, scarlet – braces?"

HOW LITTLE BO-PEEP CAME TO LOSE HER SHEEP
A Thesis

*F*or more than a century a view was held by a minority of thinkers that the Little Bo-peep story is allegorical alluding to a mystical belief system such as Quietism or Stoicism which asserts that the rhythms of the cosmos must take precedence over our own desires. Thus, "leave them alone, and they will come home bringing their tails behind them" is in the spirit of the words of Julian of Norwich, "All will be well; all manner of thing will be well." Left alone, the sheep will return intact and unhurt – a metaphor for leaving be many of life's problems.

However, recent scholarship has turned to a more frankly pastoral and less esoteric interpretation based on the belief that the Little Bo-peep rhyme may have, academically speaking, become detached from a wider corpus of similar and related work. Two aspects of this work in particular have been seen as striking.

The first is the apparent general tendency of shepherdesses to wander off and lose their sheep as demonstrated later in the Bo-peep rhyme itself:

It happened one day,
As Bo-peep did stray
Into a meadow hard by.

And in another rhyme, entitled "Bring Back Your Sheep":

I'll introduce, just wait awhile,
A charming maiden by yon stile.
"Ho! Pass this way," aloud we'll mock.
"Shepherdess, lead back your flock."

Secondly, scholars have noticed the convergence of the Bo-peep story with that of Little Boy Blue who also lost his sheep, seemingly while "under a haystack fast asleep." In fact, the link between them had clearly been recognised much earlier as evidenced in the composite nursery rhyme, "Bo-peep and Boy Blue":

If Little Bo-peep hadn't lost her sheep,
She wouldn't have had to find them.
If Little Boy Blue had not any sheep,
He wouldn't have had to mind them.

There is thus an undeniable connection between the two. But why do shepherdesses keep wandering off in this way? Is there perhaps a clue in the mocking call from the rhyme above, "Ho! Pass this way", to the "charming maiden" who is being exhorted to "lead back your flock". Are we here witnessing a little teasing by some young farm lads of a pretty shepherdess on her way to a tryst?

But can we justify such a large leap of unsubstantiated deduction? Perhaps we can when we look at yet another nursery rhyme, "Oh, where are all the Good Little Girls?"

Oh, where are all the good little girls?
Where are they all today?
And where are all the good little boys?
Tell me, somebody pray.
Oh, where the girls are, look for the boys,
Or so I've heard folk say.

So there we have it. In these Arcadian idylls the good little shepherdesses are to be found with the shepherd boys, and losing their, er, sheep in the process. In the circumstances I think it is entirely reasonable to conclude that this is exactly what happened to Little Bo-peep, and that Little Boy Blue was sleeping it off after a little rural hank-panky with her under the haystack.

"My dear! You must be just the smallest bit disappointed in the amount Uncle Harry left you, aren't you?"

"No, not really. I think I'm happy enough in the knowledge that he had his own particular set of values when it came to deciding the worth of his relatives."

"Yes, I know, dear, but doesn't it bother you just a little that you did so much more for him than I did, and yet he left me more than he left you?"

"No, it's not disappointing really. Disappointment comes when the outcome in reality falls short of one's expectations or assumptions in some way."

"And that wasn't the case in Uncle Harry's legacy to you – relative to mine, I mean?"

"No."

"How do you arrive at that view?"

"Well, as I said, it's a matter of expectation. Uncle Harry was always more susceptible to honeyed tones than to substance. So he responded more positively to your occasional gushing visits than to my more frequent stints of hum-drum housekeeping."

"Yes, perhaps. But I don't suppose one has to dress down for housekeeping quite as much as you tend to do, does one? I mean, he may have appreciated you a little more had you shown a little more glamour about the house. After all, dowdiness would hardly have cheered him up. Now would it?"

"Maybe not. But then, perhaps the converse is also true."

"What do you mean?"

"Oh, just that the overly short black cocktail dresses you wore for your infrequent morning visits probably actually prevented you from ever making his lunch. But, then, maybe that was part of the intention."

"What are you trying to say about the way I dress?"

"Only that you've never had much taste in clothes. That you've always tended towards the cheap. And, as for your perfume ... But then, that was what Uncle Harry liked, wasn't it? He didn't have much taste either. That's why I'm not disappointed. He was just acting according to his nature."

"Well! Coming from you, with your baggy jeans and unkempt hair, and smelling of the stable, that's rich. No wonder you couldn't keep your husband!"

"Of course it's no wonder! He was Uncle Harry's protégé, after all, and chosen to be his clone. Of course it's no wonder he went off drooling after a cheap tart like you. But then, you didn't keep him either, did you dear?"

"What's that supposed to mean?"

"Only that he has been with most of the women in the company. But then, of course you knew that, dear. Didn't you?"

THE CABIN BOY
A sea shanty

The boy stood on the rolling deck.
He'd been at sea a year
but, as his ship sailed into port,
he felt the pangs of fear.

"I went to sea a cabin boy,
but am I yet a man?"
his father (who was bo'sun's mate)
said, "tell me what you can."

> *"I scrubbed the decks,   (refrain – repeats every two verses)*
> *and polished brass;*
> *I served the captain's table.*
> *But, most of all,*
> *was I on call*
> *to serve his daughter Mabel.*

"She chased me up the mizzen mast,
and caught me in the hold;
then, swaying in the crow's nest,
she acted very bold.

"She caught me in amongst the shrouds,
and in between the sheets;
as I clung onto the bowsprit,
she tempted me with sweets.
     refrain
"When she found me on the yardarm,
she gave me little rest.

And once she pinned me to the floor
inside her large sea chest.

"She chased me up the spinnaker;
then from fo'c'sle to the poop.
When she'd finished in her cabin,
I was only fit to droop.
 refrain
The father gave the lad a hug.
"They've kept you on the run.
If you can satisfy them both,
you'll be a man my son."

Then Mabel flounced out on the deck –
her face was all aglow.
With heaving chest she bellowed loud;
"I want you down below!"

THE BENCH

The bench had looked comfortable enough when he first sat down, but was no longer so, especially as he bent forward for the third time on the widely spaced slats to inspect his polished shoes. No, there was still no mud on them. She was twenty-five minutes late now, and his earlier frisson of excitement was giving way to anxiety.

To his right, the path, which separated his bench from the lake beyond, curved away towards the trees on the higher ground, where the intermittent squealing of a pram wheel grated unreasonably on his nerves. The previously convivial chatter of the ducks foraging among the reeds near the lake edge had now become conspiratorial. And, behind him, the impatient bobbing and fluttering of a small boy's kite, as it struggled for height in the uncertain breeze, reflected his own feelings. His hand, on the bench back, was tight.

Yesterday in the tea-room she had seemed genuinely pleased at the prospect of seeing him again. His recollection of her hand touching his, and the smile that lit her face as they arranged the meeting, set his pulse racing again briefly. But where could she be? He should have listened to his friends, and bought a mobile phone long ago. But would she have phoned him if he had one? Did she have one? Even the ducks seemed uncertain.

From some way off rich undulating sounds rolled across the water. First a bassoon, then a clarinet, as the woodwind instrumentalists began tuning up in the Victorian bandstand confection part way around the lake. She had suggested they meet half an hour before the afternoon concert, and have tea in the lakeside café afterwards. But why had she chosen a rendezvous a quarter of a mile away? The penny rattled as it started to drop.

Earlier, in the shimmering glare of the water, he hadn't seen the other lakeside bench, much closer to the bandstand. But, now that he could, it was empty. Then he spotted someone, a female form, moving away from the bench towards the bandstand. He sprinted off the path and along the soft lakeside verge trying to keep his eyes on the figure merging with the small crowd settling into the seats. She looked around briefly before sitting in the back row, leaving a spare aisle seat beside her. But was it her? From behind he couldn't be sure.

The band had just finished playing the national anthem as he slipped panting into the empty seat, and looked down at his muddy shoes. She turned. It was her! "For heavens' sake, Dad", she whispered. "Where have you been? And just look at the state you're in! I thought you'd left me for the second time!"

SIMON'S BIRTHDAY PARTY
(The "voice" is that of Simon's mother at his
5th birthday party at home)

"Don't pull ugly faces, Jason, there's a good fellow. Can't you see it's upsetting Amanda? Besides, if the clock strikes while you're doing it, your face may stay like that …

What? Your mother says that's a fable, and shouldn't be told to children. And why do you think she says that? I seee. She says that fairy-tales and fables are harmful. And *she* knows because she's a child psychologist! I'm sure she does, Jason. But I wonder what she says about pulling ugly faces? Come along, Amanda; come and talk to Tamsin.

There we are. Aren't you two going to dancing classes together next term? Yes, I thought so. Now …

Luke! What *are* you doing? Why have you pushed your ice cream cone into Jason's ear? Yeees …, I know; because he was pulling faces at you!

Yes, I do understand, Luke. Ugly faces make you cross, but that doesn't give you the right to push ice cream into Jason's ear, now does it?

Oh, you think it does? I see. Your daddy's a soldier, and he says we must learn to stand up for ourselves. Well, I'm sure he's right, Luke, but that means defending ourselves against attack, doesn't it, and Jason didn't actually attack you, now did he?

I seee…! You think pulling faces is like attacking?

What do you think your mummy would say about that, Jason?

I'm sorry! She's your 'mother', not your 'mummy'. Yeees, I understand. She says that baby names impede our emotional development.

What does 'impede' mean, do you think?

You don't know? No, I thought not. Now, when you go home, why don't you ask her – your mother – if she thinks pulling faces is like attacking. Can you remember that, or shall I write it down for you? Nooo? You don't want me to write it down? But you *do* want to go home – *now*? Yes, of course you can, Jason – that's fine. And, yes, *I* know – too much cake is bad for you. Let's get your jacket, then, and I'll telephone for a cab to take you home.

Yes, Tamsin, what is it, dear? You can't find Amanda. Perhaps she's in the toilet? No? You think she's hiding because she didn't like the faces Jason was pulling? Alright, then; let's arrange a search party, shall we?

Now, children, we're all going to search for Amanda who's hiding somewhere. This group, on my left; you search upstairs, and the rest of us will look downstairs. And the person who finds her will get an extra helping of chocolate fudge cake. Yes, Alice? Yeees, you're in the upstairs group; but you *can* be in the downstairs group with Louise if you prefer.

Marcus! Please don't burst the balloons; we are going to need them for the games later. Off you go now, and look for Amanda.

What is it, Melanie? I think you mean 'magician', dear, not 'munition'. I see. Your mummy, I mean your mother, calls them munitions? Yeees …? And your mummy knows. I wonder if that's because, sometimes, their tricks explode? But, anyway, whatever you call them, we're not having one today. But we are going to watch a video, and theeen …, if the rain stops, we'll all go outside and play on the bouncy castle. Did you see it when you arrived? Yes? And …? Rosemary had a much bigger one at *her* party. I'm sorry about that, Melanie. Well, why don't you join the others and try to find Amanda? No? You don't like chocolate fudge cake. Very well, then; you just sit here with Jason who's waiting for a cab to take him home.

214

And, don't you pull any more faces, please, Jason!

Now, has anyone found Amanda yet? You have? That's a relief! She was under the stairs – in the coats cupboard – eating what? Eating chocolate fudge cake?

But that was for later, Amanda! For the party. Where on earth did you find it? Nooo, I'm sure you didn't find it in the coats cupboard, now did you, dear? Oh, well, never mind …

Is that your cab at the front door, Jason? No? Who is it then? Simon?

Oh, *Simon*! Just *look* at yourself! You're all wet and covered in mud. Where have you been? Outside, playing on the bouncy castle? And you fell off into the flower bed. Oh, dear, come on then, let's go upstairs and get you cleaned up …

Just a moment … *Jason*! I think the man at the front door – the one you're pulling faces at? – is the cab driver come to take you home. Do you know your address? No? Alright, I'll come with you and explain.

Now, don't you move, Simon, just stand just where you are, and try not to leave any more mud on the carpet!"

A BUNCH OF BALLOONS

*T*he chairman was hovering. He hadn't been part of the planning for the soirée, so it wasn't easy for him to find a job in the largely female hive of pre-recital activity. One of the ladies suggested that he blow up the balloons. His antipathy was palpable, even behind me, as I set out programmes. But he managed the task with not a little huffing and puffing.

"What shall I do next?" he wondered.

"Well, they need to be tied in a bunch and hung on the hedge by the gate," I murmured, placing a programme on a seat.

"No thanks," he replied. "That's a job for the ladies. They have experience of that kind of thing – children's birthday parties, and so on."

"It can't be difficult. There's some string and scissors over there."

He blanched. So I cut a four-foot length of string and tied one end around the neck of the first balloon, and then the next, and so on until all six were tied close together in a line. Then I tied the two ends of the string together and, bingo! There was a bunch!

"I don't know if that's how ladies do it for birthday parties", I said, "but I think it will look fine on the hedge by the gate."

OBJECTS OF DELIGHT

O'Neil's Café-Bar was in one of those delightful side streets off Grafton Street not far from St Stephen's Green. Inside, seated near a window, Abu Abdullah Mohammed al-Sabi al-Battani stuck out a mile. Not because of his name.

Here, in the heart of Dublin's smart shopping set, where women's fashions are the equal of Paris or Rome and the men don't usually compete, he was a replica of Aristide Bruant in Toulouse-Lautrec's famous Ambassadeurs poster. Complete with long black coat, broad-brimmed black felt hat, and flame red scarf swung nonchalantly over his shoulder, he sat quietly smoking a black Balkan Sobranie cigarette at the end of a slender ivory holder.

"Dr al-Battani?" I enquired when I reached his table.
"Ah! Dr Kelly." He beamed, his finely chisled features smiling a self-assured smile. "Please – sit down." An opulence of rings glistened on the fingers of the slim and well manicured hand that motioned me to the seat opposite him.

"Lautrec would approve, I am sure," I remarked as he ordered coffee for me.
"You mean my outfit? Oh well, one has to do something to counteract these miserable northern European winters." His manner was expansive, if not a little histrionic.

"But you're not here to discuss my sartorial eccentricities, I think. Is it not about my illustrious ancestor, Abu Mohammed al-Raqqi al-Battani, that we meet here, no?"
"That's right."
"Indeed! Five hundred years before Copernicus demonstrated that the Earth is not the centre of the Universe,

217

or even the Solar System, he computed the length of Earth's year to within two minutes of what we now know it to be. Amazing, is it not?"

"Yes it is. And I have seen what is believed to be the only remaining copy of his calculations at Padua University."

"Excellent!" He beamed again – a little too enthusiastically, I thought.

"But you say you have another copy for sale? Are there any others?"

"No, no. Not at all. What I have are his working notes – the rough calculations he polished up for presentation – for the version you saw in Padua."

"And how did you come by them?"

"They have been in the family."

"For a thousand years?"

"Certainly. Some of my family still live near Urfa in Turkey where he was born."

"But, how is it that they have not been offered to a major academic institution?"

"Well, that's exactly what I am doing now, isn't it? You say that you represent the trustees of the Chester Beatty Library here in Dublin. No?"

"OK. But what about authentication? If they've been in your family all this time there is no provenance, so we have to rely entirely on scientific and scholarly verification. Who has done that?"

"Well, the vellum and the ink have been verified by labs at Cambridge University as being consistent with the period. And the calligraphy and Arabic characters have been authenticated by a number of scholars including myself."

"Including yourself? I know that you are an expert in early Islamic manuscripts, but doesn't having a financial interest in the transaction invalidate your evidence?"

"Well, mine was just the icing on the cake. You see, I was able to certify that some of the embellishments in the text were peculiar to the towns of Antioch and Ar-Raqqah in Syria during the time he worked there in the early 11th century."

"What were they exactly, these embellishments?"

"Have a look here," he said taking from his briefcase a photocopy of a document in Arabic script. "Do you see these lovely little shapes with beautiful double-curves beneath some of the main characters? They are known as callipygeans, and were used very briefly only in that region during a short-lived dialect around that time. So, you see, that fixes the document both in time and place."
I frowned, and he looked at me quizzically.

"You have a question?"
"Yes I have. Did you say callipygeans?" I asked.
"Yes, of course, callipygeans." A flicker of concern passed briefly across his aristocratic features, still smiling, but now appealingly innocent. "Why do you ask?"
"Well, because it causes me to question the authenticity of the original document."
"Really? How so?"
"Dr al-Battani, I am not an expert in early Islamic manuscripts. My subject is Classical sculpture. And, while there may be a charming aesthetic connection with the shape of the beautiful double-curves on your manuscript, it probably ends there. 'Callipygean' is in fact an adjective and comes from the Greek *Kallipygos*. It was applied specifically to the goddess Aphrodite, and it means 'having beautifully proportioned buttocks!'"

THE SUNDAY SCHOOL PICNIC

"Good morning, Vicar. Good of you to come
and see us off. The kids appreciate
you turning out. We're due to leave quite soon;
but have you seen Melissa? No? She should
be here by now. John, come on dear, and get
inside the coach. Oh, I see. You've dropped your
marbles on the pavement and you're trying
to pick them up. And, have you got them now?
You have? That's good. Then come along, now there's
a dear. Oh look, here comes Melissa now
with her mother in their four-by-four. Good
morning, Mrs Owen-Jones! Yes I know;
the traffic's awful at this time of day,
especially when you're half a block away.
Now, Jason, please! Don't pull Patricia's hair.
I know she left her picnic basket on
the floor. Yeees, I saw you trip, but that's no
excuse for hurting her like that. So just
let go and help her put the basket on
the shelf. Then sit down next to Jeremy
back there. Nooo, not by Mary. Further back,
I said – by Jeremy. Yeees, that's him there
in front of Andrew. There, Melissa dear,
there isn't any need to cry now, is
there? Your mother wasn't really late, and
we waited for you, didn't we? Now dry
your tears, and sit there next to Mandy where
I can see you. Yes, Jemima, they have
a great big lake at Hever Castle and
lots of lovely grassy banks for picnics.
Andrew, don't do that. Here, take this tissue

and wipe your nose on that instead. Josie,
put away your picnic box, please; it isn't
time for eating yet. Now, look! You've dribbled
trifle on your skirt. Just wait a moment
and I'll wipe it up. Now, children, are we
all aboard and in our seats with seat-belts
fastened? Yes, I think we are. So, alright driver;
sorry for the wait. You can close the doors –
off at last to Hever. Oh, Good Heavens!
Stop the coach! There's John outside again. He's
looking round for his bloody marbles!"

The man sitting on the bench near the Padstow quay was wearing a fawn suit, brown plaid shirt and a diagonally striped tan and yellow tie. He had a walking stick between his knees.

"Mind if I sit down?", I asked.

"Suit yourself", he mumbled absently. He was watching a seagull strutting towards him.

"Thank you."

"No probs. What I always say is …"

I wasn't sure whether his pause was intended to increase the dramatic effect of the wisdom he was about to impart, or to give himself time to remember what it was that he always said. I decided it was the seagull.

"… do unto others as …", he continued sermonically when the seagull stopped.

"Thanks. I know the rest. I sometimes wonder why we indulge in these ritualised courtesies."

"Wad'ya mean?"

"Well, this is a Padstow Council bench, and there was plenty of spare space beside you. Is it a British thing, do you think, to ask permission to sit down?"

His eyes glazed over. The seagull was close to his feet.

"How should I know. I don't bother with questions like that. What I say is, live and let live."

As he spoke he took a swipe at the offending bird with his stick. It fluttered up and dropped nonchalantly onto a coiled chain just out of reach, then squawked at him insolently. He poked two fingers into the air in retalliation.

"I saw you sitting here yesterday. Do you come here frequently?"

"Every morning."

"It must be marvellous to sit here and watch the harbour changing with the tides and seasons."

"Can't say I ever noticed. I just come here until the wife has finished the housework."

"Oh, I see. And then?"

"At eleven I go home for my morning tea and a look at the papers."

"Every morning – at eleven?"

"Yes. That's why I give her a noo hoover for Christmas – so she can finish the housework by eleven. I can't stand the noise of the hoover when I'm trying to read the papers."

The seagull spotted a morsel near his feet and retrieved it deftly while simultaneously hopping aside to avoid the flailing stick.

"I hate those damn' gulls!", he snapped absently.

The bird eyed him balefully before floating off the quay edge to join his companions below pecking in the mud between the mooring ropes and lolling boats in the low tide harbour.

"Don't you ever go to the Harbour Café over there for your morning tea?"

"Nah, they don't do toasted tea-cakes in there."

"No? That's surprising."

"Nah. I must have a toasted tea-cake with my morning tea. That's why I bought the wife a special tea-cake toaster for her birthday."

"Really? And, while you're reading the papers – I suppose your wife prepares lunch then?"

"No, that's when she does the shopping – after she's washed up the tea things o'course. And on the way home she calls in to the chippy and picks up some fish and chips for my lunch."

"Have you ever tried Rick Stein's fish and chip shop round the corner from here?"

"Nah. He's German in't he? I don't like Germans. And, besides, what do they know about fish and chips?"

I stood up.

"I hope you enjoy your morning tea – and your toasted tea-cake."

But he didn't hear me. He was thrashing at another seagull.

THE MOBILE PHONE CONVERSATION

"Hello darling. It's me.

Where am I? I'm on the train. On the way home.

Well, no, not exactly – at Waterloo.

No, it hasn't actually left yet. We're still in the station …

What? Oh, in about two minutes I should think.

Yes, darling, I know what time it is. It's nearly nine-twenty. I had to run most of the way to the station, and just made the train. That's why I couldn't phone you before.

I know my mobile's been switched off. And I'm sorry it's so late, but I was in a meeting with some of the other fund managers in the bank.

Yes, I know it's Christmas Eve tomorrow but, with the time difference between here and New York, we had a lot of work to get through before the holiday.

Okay, you phoned the office at five fifteen, and I wasn't there. Sorry, I should have explained that we had our meeting in a wine bar.

Yes, we often do that. Less stressful than being in the office.

Which one? Oh, our usual one. Pavarotti's, just off Lombard Street. Why?

You phoned there too. What time was that?

At six-thirty. Well, it must have been the other wine bar then. You know, the one around the corner from Pavarotti's. Yes, I remember now. Of course it was. Pavarotti's was pretty busy, so we went round to The Bottle Stopper.

You don't believe me? For heaven's sake, darling, why not?

Of course I haven't been with another woman. Which one, for goodness' sake?

Oh, come on; now you're being silly. 'Which one?' was a figure of speech. Of course I haven't any number of women to choose from.

Okay, yes, I know, it happened once before. But that was long ago, and it was the only time.

No, it never happened again.

What do you mean, am I sure? Naturally I'm sure.

Of course I can't prove it, darling You can't prove a negative!

No, I'm not trying to be a smart arse. I'm just trying to explain. Look, the train's about to go.

Of course I care, but what can I do if you don't believe me?

Sorry, the train's making a noise over the points ...

What did you say about dinner? Andy and Megan? What are they doing there?

The celebration dinner before Andy's posting abroad in January. Oh, Lord!, I forgot.

What did you say? They've been there since seven-thirty? Oh, that's terrible.

Champagne? What champagne?

I was supposed to... Oh bugger! Yes I was, wasn't I?

What's that? You're going to get an Indian take-away?

What for? Why don't you just have your dinner now? Don't worry about me.

You can't because the dinner's spoilt. Look, I'm really sorry about all this. I'll make it up somehow.

Sorry, the train's making a noise again ...

What? You're going to spend the night with Andy and Megan, and have your meal there.

Why ever would you want to do that?

Well, if you feel that's what you want to do, what can I do about it?

You see; there you go again. Of course I care. Look, I said I'm sorry, but if you're really going to spend the night with Andy and Megan, can you please leave a key under the mat for me. I haven't got my house keys with me.

Come on now, don't be silly. You can't lock me out! Wait! Where will I sleep if you ...?"

PASSING TRAINS

A guard's shrill whistle announced the imminent departure of the train on the next platform and, with no other movement than the slight collapse of the broadsheet newspaper opposite me, one of the podgy but beautifully manicured male hands that had been holding it detached itself and poked two fingers into the air in a gesture of unfocused retaliation.

But his movement attracted my attention to the exquisite flatness of the paper. Almost, it appeared, and then I realised that, yes, it had actually been, ironed. Not only that but, as I could see from the fine folds, it had been ironed in half as well, possibly by a long-suffering wife I wondered, when she was ironing into his black pin-stripe suit trousers the sharpest creases I had ever seen.

A second whistle, the train's own this time, as it began to move, caused a greater, but remarkably controlled, reaction. With his face a mask of studied calm, he closed his paper very deliberately tapping all the edges carefully to ensure that the pages were precisely aligned, then he folded it meticulously along the crease line and slammed it onto his lap.

"Bloody noise!" he barked angrily at the adjacent train as it rattled and squeaked its way out of the station.

"Do you travel on this train every day?" I enquired.

"Yes", he replied as he checked his tie for alignment, and flicked an imaginary speck of dust from his lapel. "The 7.36 from Milton Bassett, every morning for the last thirty-two ...

no, I tell a lie, it will be thirty-three years next month – on the 16th to be exact. I've written to them many times, you know, the management, that is, about the noise. But you know how it is these days; nobody cares or takes any responsibility."

He adjusted the pink carnation in his button hole.

"What did they say?"

"Well, the kind of platitudes you would expect. Trains and train whistles cannot be made silent. I mean to say, what nonsense." He checked his pocket watch against the station clock. "See what I mean. They can't even get the time right. It's all these immigrants of course." He patted the perfectly folded scarlet handkerchief in his breast pocket. "Untrustworthy and feckless lot, I say. Been saying so for years. They're just not like us of course; don't have our values," he continued as he tugged at his trouser legs to release the tension at his tight-together knees.

"Standards are slipping all over. Even in the literary world. I had to reject a manuscript recently from a well-known writer of children's stories."

"Why was that?"

"Punctuation."

"Punctuation? But don't publishers have editorial people who check that kind of thing?"

"Well, yes, but if a well-known author can't get it right in the first place it's unprofessional."

"What kind of errors were they?"

"Mrs Furry Tail the rabbit." He stroked the edges of his finely trimmed moustache with a curled forefinger to add gravitas to his reply. "In one place in the text 'Mrs' is spelt with a full-stop, and in another without."

"Would children notice that, do you think? I mean, is it important?"

"Vital" he snapped, straightening his gold tie-pin "Vital, if professionalism is to be respected."

A fast InterCity train flew past, its whistle wailing. He snorted as two involuntary fingers prodded the air in protest. Then he snatched his newspaper from his lap and opened it with such venom that it tore apart precisely down the finely ironed crease.

"Damnation! See what I mean. They can't even produce decent newsprint anymore!"

"Windows flicker; images are fleeting.
Far ahead the locomotive whistles
as a blur of lights is disappearing round the bend;
smoke and steam still gusting round the platform;
in the darkness buzzing tracks fall silent."